Catalog of
Published Concert Music
by
American Composers

Second Supplement
to the Second edition

by

Angelo Eagon

The Scarecrow Press, Inc.
Metuchen, N. J.   1974

ISBN 0-8108-0728-9

Library of Congress Catalog Card Number 68-9327

FOREWORD

This Supplement (No. 2) of the <u>Catalog of Published Concert Music by American Composers</u> (second edition) brings the entries up-to-date as of November 1, 1973.

Together with the Second Edition and with the (First) Supplement to that edition, published respectively by The Scarecrow Press in July 1969 and in August 1971, this Second Supplement is a current reference for the extensive repertory of concert music by American composers, including works in various categories which are generally available in some printed form for purchase. In time, many of the works listed in these references will be out of print, but the catalogs can always serve those doing research in the field of American music.

In compiling the catalogs, I had to make an arbitrary decision on what constitutes an "American" composer. The following criteria were established: in addition to works by native-born composers, I have listed works by those foreign-born composers who became naturalized American citizens before the age of 26 and who have made significant contributions to the American musical scene.

The format and the general organization follow that of the Second Edition and of the (First) Supplement.

I shall always be indebted to the many music publishers with whom I have worked closely in compiling these catalogs for their cooperation and assistance.

Special Notice

Included in the (First) Supplement (1971) was an "Addendum to Supplement No. 1," on pages 115 to 130--this Addendum did not appear on the "Table of Contents" to that volume but its contents were indexed. The works listed in that Addendum are not repeated in this Second Supplement.

Angelo Eagon
Professor of Music
Colorado Women's College
Denver, Colorado
November 1, 1973

TABLE OF CONTENTS

*With piano unless otherwise indicated
†All durations or timings are approximate

KEY TO ABBREVIATIONS

A	alto voice	cor	cornet
acc	accompaniment	dr	drum or drums
acdn	accordion	E-hn	English horn
a-cl	alto clarinet	fl	flute
a-fl	alto flute	full	full symphony orch.
a-rec or rec(A)	alto recorder	glock	glockenspiel
		gtr	guitar
a-sax	alto saxophone	high	high voice
anon	anonymous	hn	French horn
arr	arrang-ed, -ment	har	harmonica
B	bass voice	hp	harp
b-rec or rec(B)	bass recorder	hpcd	harpsichord
		instr	instrument(s), --al, --ation
Bar	baritone voice	low	low voice
bar	baritone horn	man	mandolin
bar-sax	baritone saxophone	mar	marimba
B-Bar	bass baritone voice	med	medium voice
b-cl	bass clarinet	min	minutes (approximate duration)
b-dr	bass drum		
bsn	bassoon	mov	movement(s)
b-trb	bass trombone	m-S	mezzo soprano voice
clav	clavichord	ms	manuscript
c-b	contra bass, double bass	mu	mute
c-bsn	contra bassoon	NA	not available
cel	celesta	Narr	narrator
cent	century	ob	oboe
ch	chorus	obb	obbligato
cham	chamber orchestra	opt	optional
cl	clarinet	orch	full orchestra
cmb	cymbals	org	organ
Col	coloratura voice	perc	percussion

picc	piccolo	unspec	unspecified
pno	piano	vib	vibraphone
pt	parts	vla	viola
(R)	parts on rental	vlc	violoncello
rec	recorder	vln	violin
rev	revised or revision	xy	xylophone
S	soprano voice		
SATB	mixed chorus (Soprano, Alto, Tenor, Bass)		
sax	saxophone		
sc	scenes		
sec	section		
sn-dr	snare drum		
Sp	speaker		
s-rec or rec(S)	soprano recorder		
SSA	women's chorus (Sopranos I & II, Alto)		
str	strings		
str qrt	string quartet		
susp	suspended		
sym	symphony		
tam	tambourine		
T	tenor voice		
t-dr	tenor drum		
tba	tuba		
timp	timpani		
trad	traditional		
trans	translator or translation		
trb	trombone		
tri	triangle		
trp	trumpet		
t-rec or rec(T)	tenor recorder		
t-sax	tenor saxophone		
t-trb	tenor trombone		
TTBB	men's chorus (Tenors I & II, Basses I & II)		
unacc	unaccompanied		

viii

1. VOICE

SOLO (piano accompaniment unless otherwise indicated)

Composer, Title & Publisher	Range	Author of Text

The AMERICAN musical miscellany
(Northampton, Mass., 1798)
(H. Wiley Hitchcock, Ed.) DCP
A collection of 111 songs published
the year before George Washington
died. "A general preference has
been given to American produc-
tions," wrote the editors, who
aimed to present the songs, "which,
from general consent, are now in
vogue. "

ARGENTO, Dominick
Letters from composers (with
   guitar) B&H   high
    1. Frederic Chopin to a friend,
       Palma, 28 December 1838
    2. Wolfgang Amadeus Mozart to
       his father, Vienna, 9 June
       1781
    3. Franz Schubert to a friend,
       Vienna, 31 March 1824
    4. Johann Sebastian Bach to the
       Town Council, Leipzig, 24
       August 1736
    5. Claude Debussy to a friend,
       Le Molleau, 3 December 1916
    6. Giocomo Puccini to a friend,
       Paris, 10 May 1898
    7. Robert Schumann to his
       fiancée, Leipzig, 3 June 1839

BABBITT, Milton
  Vision & prayer (with synthesized   S   Dylan Thomas
    accompaniment (R) AMP

BARAB, Seymour
  The rivals TP   high   James Stephens
    The daisies. The rose in
      the wind. The hawk. The
      rivals.

Composer, Title & Publisher	Range	Author of Text
BAVICCHI, John		
Six Korean folk songs in a contemporary setting, Op. 35 SEM	med	trad
1. Miryang Arirang		
2. Nohdle Kahngbyun		
3. Pang ah Iahryung		
4. Toraji Tahryung		
5. Arirang		
6. Pahgyun Pokpo		
To the lighthouse, Op. 16 (with horn & piano) SEM	S	Norma Farber
Trio no. 3, Op. 18 (with violin & cello) SEM	S	vocalise
BECK, John Ness		
Song of joy, adapted from Psalm 40 CFP	high	Biblical
BENSON, Warren		
Shadow wood MCA (with piano or wind ensemble)	S	Tennessee Williams
1. Shadow wood		
2. My little one		
3. Old men are fond		
4. Covenant		
5. The last wine		
BEVERIDGE, Thomas		
Songs of praise (13 hymns & responses) ECS	med	
(For contents & authors of texts, see "Chorus--Women's")		
BOCK, Fred		
When Adam was created (a wedding song) TP	med	trad; adapted by Erna Moorman
BRADLEY, Ruth		
Abraham Lincoln walks at midnight (a cantata) CPI	med	Vachel Lindsay
Bleeker Street market (with chimes ad lib) CPI	med	Emily Barto
CARTER, Elliott		
Tell me where is fancy bred (with guitar) AMP	low	Shakespeare
CHADWICK, George W. (H. Wiley Hitchcock, Ed.)		
Songs to poems by Arlo Bates, 1892, 1897 DCP		
A selection from the more than 100 songs by this Bostonian, long-time Director of the New England Conservatory and one of the most gifted and versatile composers of		

Voice: Solo

Composer, Title & Publisher	Range	Author of Text

the late 19th century. Arlo Bates,
1850-1918, was teacher of English at M. I. T. and author of fic-
tion and verse.

CIVIL War songs (H. Wiley Hitchcock, Ed.) DCP
A volume reprinting popular songs
from both sides of the War be-
tween the States, by such composers as Henry Clay Work
("Kingdom coming"), George
Root ("The battle cry of free-
dom"), Dan Emmett ("Dixie's
land"), and Patrick Gilmore
("When Johnny comes marching
home").

COLGRASS, Michael
New people (with viola & piano) m-S Michael Colgrass
MCA

CRUMB, George
Ancient voices of children (a S & boy-S García Lorca
cycle of songs) CFP
(with electric piano, oboe,
mandolin, harp & percussion
--3 players)
I. El niño busca su voz (The
little boy was looking for
his voice)
"Dances of the ancient earth"
II. Me he perdido muchas veces
por el mar (I have lost my-
self in the sea many times)
III. ¿De donde vienes, amor, mi
niño? (From where do you
come, my love, my child?)
"Dance of the sacred life-
cycle"
IV. Todas las tardes en Granada,
todas las tardes se muere
un niño (Each afternoon in
Granada, a child dies each
afternoon)
"Ghost dance"
V. Se ha llenado de luces mi
corazón de seda (My heart
of silk is filled with lights)

De GASTYNE, Serge
Deux chansons Françaises FER med
(with flute & vibraharp)
1. A la forêt de Gastine   Pierre de Ronsard
2. Il bacio   Paol Verlaine
Rondel (with vibraharp) FER med Charles d'Orléans;
trans: Henry W.
Longfellow

Composer, Title & Publisher	Range	Author of Text
Two songs on Tanka poems (with vibraharp) FER	med	
1. Falling from the ridge		Emperor Yōzei
2. Like a wave crest		Emperor Uda
DELLO JOIO, Norman		
Lamentation of Saul (with orchestra(R)) CF	Bar	Biblical
Songs of Abelard EBM	med	Abelard
DEL TREDICI, David		
Six songs from James Joyce B&H	S	James Joyce
1. My dove		
2. Monotone		
3. Bahnhofstrasse		
4. A flower given to my daughter		
5. Alone		
6. She weeps over Rahoon		
Night conjure verse (with string quartet & woodwind septet) B&H	S or m-S or counter T	James Joyce
1. Simples		
2. A memory of the players in a mirror at midnight		
DIAMOND, David		
Christmas tree EV	med	e. e. cummings
Do I love you? (Theme & variations) SMPC	med	Jack Larson
Hebrew melodies SMPC	med	Lord Byron
1. My soul is dark		
2. If that high world		
3. Saul		
4. All is vanity (ciaccona)		
Homage to Paul Klee EV	med	Babette Deutsch
I am rose EV	med	Gertrude Stein
Life and death SMPC	low	Chidiock Tichborne (16th cent)
Love and time (a song cycle) SMPC	med	Katie Louchheim
1. The incredible hour		
2. Whither thou goest		
3. Love's worth		
4. Spring talk		
The millenium SMPC	low	Isak Dinesen
Ode SMPC	med	Arthur W. E. O'Shaughnessy
DINERSTEIN, Norman		
Four settings for soprano & string quartet B&H	S	Emily Dickinson
I. Dying		
II. The bustle in the house		
III. Apparently with no surprise		
IV. I died for beauty		

Composer, Title & Publisher	Range	Author of Text
EHLE, Robert C.		
Algorhythms (with prepared piano, clarinet & bass) CF	S	Robert C. Ehle
ELMORE, Robert		
Arise, my love CPI	med	from Song of Solomon
FLAGELLO, Nicolas		
As I walked forth GEN	med	William Blake
O father, O father GEN	med	William Blake
This frog he would a-wooing ride GEN	med	William Blake

FOSTER, Stephen (H. Wiley Hitch-
cock, Ed.)
   Household songs   DCP
   A selection, reprinted from the
      early sheet music editions, of
      songs for the mid-nineteenth
      century parlor by America's
      first great song writer.   Along
      with such familiar songs as
      "Jeanie with the light brown hair"
      and "Beautiful dreamer" appear
      less well-known ones like "Ah,
      may the red rose live alway,"
      "Open thy lattice, love," and
      "Happy hours at home."

HANSON, Howard		
Four psalms for baritone CF	Bar	Biblical

HAUSSERMANN, John		
Five singing miniatures, Op. 12 CPI	med, high	
Black moon		John Haussermann
Death		From the Arabian; trans: by E. Powys Mathers
Oread		Hilda Doolittle
Perhaps I'll come		Wanda Marine van Hosen
The waterlilly		Robert M. B. Nicols
Three moods, Op. 18 CPI	med	John Haussermann
At Eastertide. Return. The wind and the song		

HEINRICH, Anthony Philip (H. Wiley
Hitchcock, Ed.)
   The dawning of music in Kentucky
      & The Western minstrel (1820)
      DCP
   A volume of works selected from the
      enormous output of this immigrant
      composer known in the 1820's as
      "the Beethoven of America." He
      characterized his own music, as
      found in publications like The

Composer, Title & Publisher	Range	Author of Text

dawning of music in Kentucky
and The Western minstrel (both
1820), as "full of strange somer-
sets and capriccios. "

HERDER, Ronald
 Requiem II: games of power   m-S   Giacomo Leopardi;
  (with men's chorus, chamber   trans: John Heath-
  ensemble, electronic tape &   Stubbs & Iris Origo
  percussion (R)) AMP
  (See also "Chorus--Men's"; "(Instr
  Ensemble) String--with Voice,
  Winds, and/or Percussion"; &
  "Percussion")

HILLER, Lejaren & R. Baker
 Computer cantata (with instrumental   med   Lejaren Hiller
  ensemble & 2-channel tape re-
  corder) NME

HORVIT, Michael
 Three songs of elegy ECS   S   Emily Dickinson
  1. I felt a cleavage in my mind
  2. Ample make this bed
  3. I felt a funeral in my brain

HOVHANESS, Alan
 Canticle (with oboe, xylophone,   S   Alan Hovhaness
  celesta, harp, strings) CFP
  1. Pastoral
  2. Song "Over autumn lake"
  3. Song "Thick fog on river"
  4. Song "Melancholy rain"
 Saturn (with Clarinet & Piano) CFP   S   Alan Hovhaness
  Prelude. From Titan. Orb
  mysterious.
  Saturn, celestial globe. O lost
  note.
  My hymn. Giant globe. Vision of
  Saturn. On wings of soundless
  note.
  What is universe? Intermezzo.
  Harp of Saturn

IVEY, Jean
 Terminus (with 2-channel tape) CF   m-S   Jean Ivey

JONES, Marjorie
 Four short solos TP   med   Adelaide Crapsey
  1. On seeing weather-beaten
    trees
  2. November night
  3. Triad
  4. Little sister Rose-Marie

Composer, Title & Publisher	Range	Author of Text
KELLY, Earl 　Rue François Premier　CPI	med	Robert Hillyer
KREBS, Stanley 　Cleopatra's farewell　CPI	high	Florence Bryant
LADERMAN, Ezra 　From the Psalms　OX 　　What I did not steal.　Behold the 　　wicked man.　From the end of 　　the earth.　Look away from me. 　　Thou didst set the earth	S	Biblical
LA MONTAINE, John 　Bird's courting song　GAL	med	trad
LEKBERG, Sven 　A ballad of the trees and the 　　master　GAL	high	Sidney Lanier
LEVY, Marvin David 　One person　B&H	A　orch(R)	Elinor Wylie
LYBBERT, Donald 　From harmonium (song cycle) 　　TP 　Another weeping woman.　The 　death of a soldier.　To the 　roaring wind.　Valley candle	high	Wallace Stevens
MOORE, Douglas 　Adam was my grandfather　GAL	med	Stephen Vincent Benét
MOSS, Lawrence 　Three Rilke songs　SEM 　　1. Da neight Sich die Stunde 　　　(How the hour bows down) 　　2. Erkleute sind wir (We are 　　　all workmen) 　　3. Was wirst du tun, Gott, wenn 　　　ich sterbe (What will you 　　　do, God, when I die)	m-S	Rainer Maria Rilke; 　trans: Babette 　Deutsch
PARCHMAN, Gen 　"Cycle of novelties"　SEM 　　1. It couldn't be done 　　2. The flea 　　3. Resume 　　4. Little lamb 　　5. Just and the unjust 　　6. I remember	S	 Gen Parchman Roland Young Dorothy Parker William Blake Lord Bomen Thomas Hood
PASATIERI, Thomas 　Heloise and Abelard　BEL/MIL 　Selected songs　SMPC	S, Bar	Louis Philips

Composer, Title & Publisher	Range	Author of Text
Three American Songs	med	Louis Philips
1. Boundaries		
2. Haiku		
3. Critic's privilege		
Two Shakespeare songs	med	Shakespeare
1. Parting		
2. That time of year (Sonnet 13)		
Three coloratura songs	high	
1. Miranda--Miranda		Louis Philips
2. Lear and his daughters		Louis Philips
3. Love's emblems		John Fletcher
PERSICHETTI, Vincent		
A net of fireflies (song cycle) EV	med	trans: Harold Steward
Waking at the inn (Sôseki)		
The pavilion on the lake (Rimpû)		
With sharpened senses (Bashô)		
Four magpies (Hô-ô)		
A whiteness (Shikô)		
Noon (Buson)		
The carp (Raizan)		
The faun (Issa)		
Hypothesis (Zen Paradox)		
Summer grasses (Bashô)		
Paper wings (Hô-ô)		
Its netted trail (Hô-ô)		
Beneath the net (Buson-Sôgyo)		
Firefly (Bashô)		
After the death of her small son		
(Chiyo)		
Dewdrop (Issa)		
The black cat's face (Hô-ô)		
PINKHAM, Daniel		
Man, that is born of a woman	m-S	Book of Common Prayer
(with guitar) ECS		
RAPHLING, Sam		
Shadows in the sun GEN	med	Langston Hughes
READ, Gardner		
All day I hear B&H	med	James Joyce
Lullaby for a man child GAL	med	Jean Starr Untermeyer
RECK, David		
Night sounds (and dream) (with	S	e. e. cummings
percussion & contrabass) CPE		
RILEY, Dennis		
Five songs on Haiku texts CFP	S	Haiku texts
ROCHBERG, George		
Eleven songs TP	m-S	Paul Rochberg
1. Sunrise, a morning sound		
2. We are like the mayflies		
3. I am baffled by this wall		

Composer, Title & Publisher	Range	Author of Text

4. Spectral butterfly
5. All my life
6. Le sacre du printemps
7. Black tulips
8. Nightbird berates
9. So late!
10. Angel's wing (ballad)
11. How to explain (ballad)

Two songs from "Tableaux" TP   med   Paul Rochberg
  1. Ballad
  2. Nightpiece

ROREM, Ned
Ariel (song cycle)   S   Sylvia Plath
  (with clarinet)
  B&H
Gloria B&H   2 solo voices   liturgical
  1. Gloria in excelsis Deo
  2. Laudamus te
  3. Domine Deus
  4. Miserere nobis
  5. Qui tollis...
  6. Qui sedes...
  7. Interlude
  8. Cadenza
  9. Quoniam tu solus
King Midas (a cantata) B&H   T, S   Howard Moss
  1. The king's speech
  2. The queen's song
  3. The princess' speech
  4. The queen's speech
  5. The huntsman's song, the
    gardener's refrain
  6. Address by Dionysus
  7. The princess' song
  8. The king's song
  9. Dionysus' song
  10. The king to the princess, at
    the river bank
  King Midas may be performed by
  one singer but, ideally, by two,
  with the poems divided as follows:
    1, 5, 6, 8, 9, 10 --Tenor
    2, 3, 4, 7--Soprano
  However, up to 4 voices may be
  used, distributed as follows:
    King Midas, Tenor; queen (and
    the gardener) m-Soprano;
    princess, Soprano; huntsman,
    Baritone
Last poems B&H   med   Wallace Stevens
  (with cello & piano)
War scenes B&H   med   Walt Whitman
  1. A night battle
  2. Specimen case
  3. An incident

Composer, Title & Publisher	Range	Author of Text

  4. Inauguration ball
  5. The real war will never get
     in the books
Poèmes pour la paix B&H   med
(with piano or orch. (R))
  1. Lay   Jehan Regnier (1392-
                                                1470)
  2. Ode   Pierre de Ronsard
                                                (1524-1585)
  3. Sonnet I   Olivier de Magny (1529-
                                                1560)
  4. Sonnet II   Olivier de Magny
  5. Sonnet   Jean Daurat (1505-1588)
  6. Hymn of peace   Jean Antoine de Baif
                                                (1532-1589)

Six Irish songs SMPC   med   George Darley (1795-
(with piano or orch (R))   1846)
  1. Lay of the forlorn
  2. Robin's cross
  3. Chorus of spirits
  4. The call of the morning
  5. Runilda's chant
  6. The sea ritual

SACCO, P. Peter
  Collected songs, vol. 1 WIM
    Daybreak (also with string   med   Henry W. Longfellow
      orch (R))
    Deceive me once again   med   Walter Savage Landor
      (also with string orch (R))
    Four early songs
      1. She walks in beauty   med   Lord Byron
      2. She dwelt among untrodden med   William Wordsworth
        ways
      3. When you are old   low   William Butler Yeats
      4. Tears, idle tears   low   Alfred Lord Tennyson
    The Lord is my shepherd   med   Biblical
      (Psalm 23)
    Moments   low   Earl Jones
    The moon is rising   med   Early Chinese poem;
                                                trans: Robert Payne
    The rain falls   med   Edward Hoy
    Snow falling   low   anon; trans: Leon
                                                Zolbrod
    Song of the brook   med   Alfred Lord Tennyson
    That silent land   med   Edward Hoy
      (also with string orch (R))
    Three Psalms (with brass   T or S   Biblical
      quintet) WIM
      1. Psalm 13: How long wilt Thou
        forget me, O Lord
      2. Psalm 18: The sorrows of
        death
      3. Psalm 83: Keep not Thou
        silence, O God

Voice: Solo   11

Composer, Title & Publisher	Range	Author of Text
STRICKLAND, William		
A flower given to my daughter GAL	med	James Joyce
Ione, dead the long year GAL	med	Ezra Pound
She weeps for Rahoon GAL	med	James Joyce
THOMSON, Virgil		
The following two collections were listed in the Catalog of Concert Music by American Composers, page 47, 2nd Edition (1969), but are now available from SMPC:		
"Five songs from William Blake" (also with orch)		
"Four songs to the poems of Thomas Campion" (with piano or clarinet, viola & harp)		
Le singe et la leopard (The monkey and the leopard) fable de la Fontaine SMPC	med	La Fontaine
Portrait of F. B. (Frances Blood) GS	med	Gertrude Stein
THORNE, Francis		
Magnificat JC	med	liturgical
Nocturnes JC	med	Francis Thorne
Nunc dimittis JC	med	liturgical
WARD-STEINMAN, David		
Fragments from Sappho EBM (with flute & clarinet obbligato)	S	Sappho; trans: Mary Barnard
WHEAR, Paul W.		
From Thoreau (with violin) MEDP	med	Henry David Thoreau
WORK, Henry Clay		
Songs of Henry Clay Work (1832-1884) (H. Wiley Hitchcock, Ed.) DCP		
WYNER, Yehudi		
Psalms & early songs AMP	med	
1. Psalm 119		Biblical
2. Psalm 66		Biblical
3. When you are old		W. Butler Yeats
4. Exeunt		Richard Wilbur

CHORUS--MIXED (SATB a cappella unless otherwise indicated)

Composer, Title and Publisher	Chorus	Solo	Accompaniment	Author of Text
AHROLD, Frank There was the door JF	SSATTB		finger cmb, tri, gong, vib, 2 fl	Omar Khảyyảm
ALBERT, Stephen Bacchae (a ceremony in concert) GS		Narr	electric gtr, sax & orch(R)	Euripides
ALEXANDER, Josef Hosanna L-G				liturgical
ALLCOCK, Stephen Credo B&H				Edwin Arlington Robinson
AVSHALOMOV, Jacob Praises from the corners of the earth MCA			org, perc	
1. Heare us, Lord				John Donne
2. By the noon-day brightness				The Koran
3. O thou great mystery				Chief Joseph Strongwolf
4. I thank you, God				e. e. cummings
Prophecy ECS		Cantor	org	Biblical
BAKSA, Robert And will you leave me so? B&H				Sir Thomas Wyatt
Crabbed-age and youth (madrigal) AB				Shakespeare
Full fathom five (madrigal) AB				Shakespeare
My soul doth magnify the Lord TP				Biblical
Psalm 13 SMPC		T	org or pno	Biblical
BALLARD, Louis W. The gods will hear (a cantata on the origins of Indians on the American continent) BI			pno & perc	Based on poem, "Man is here, here is man," by Lloyd H. New

Composer, Title and Publisher	Chorus	Solo	Accompaniment	Author of Text
BANKS, Robert				
The praise chorale (a Negro folk-gospel cantata) BEL/MIL			pno	Biblical
1. Oh, praise His holy name				
2. The rivers of Babylon				
3. Strong deliverer				
4. Land of peace				
5. The amen song				
BARBER, Samuel				
The lovers, Op. 43 GS		Bar	orch(R)	Based on "Twenty love poems and a song of despair" by Pablo Neruda; trans: Christopher Logue & W.S. Merwin
BASSETT, Leslie				
Collect WLP			electronic tape	anon
Moon canticle CFP		Narr	vlc obb	A composite of sources & fragments from Milton, Shelley, Sidney, Harley, Theocritus, Shakespeare, Thompson, Bassett, Joaquin Miller, Sir Richard Burton, Keats
1. Introduction				
2. Query				
3. Incantation				
4. Forecast				
5. Conclusion				
BAVICCHI, John				
Fly hence, shadows (in: Choral art) NAK				John Ford (1586-1639)
BECK, John Ness				
The sunlit hour TP			pno	John Ness Beck
Three Prophecies from Isaiah NAK				Biblical
Cry aloud. And in that day. Ye shall go out with joy. (Above are published separately)				
Variants on an Irish hymn (Be Thou my vision) TP			pno or org, sn-dr or band(R) or orch(R)	Ancient Irish from the Poem Book of the Gael
The young lions (adapted from Psalm 104) TP			pno or org	Biblical
BENNETT, Claudia				
Three improvisations MEDP			cham & 2 pno	Claudia Bennett

Composer, Title and Publisher	Chorus	Solo	Accompaniment	Author of Text
BERNSTEIN, Leonard				
Mass (a theater piece for singers, players & dancers) GS	varies	T(with leading role as the Celebrant); other soloists in all voices.	orch (R) & electronic tape	liturgy of the Roman Mass; additional texts by Stephen Schwartz & Leonard Bernstein
I. Devotions before the mass				
II. First introit				
III. Second introit				
IV. Confession				
V. Meditation No. 1				
VI. Gloria				
VII. Meditation No. 2				
VIII. Epistle				
IX. Gospel sermon				
X. Credo				
XI. Meditation No. 3				
XII. Offertory				
XIII. The Lord's prayer				
XIV. Sanctus				
XV. Agnus Dei				
XVI. Fraction				
XVII. Pax: Communion				
BETTS, Donald				
As the hart panteth (Psalm 42) AMP				Biblical
BEVERSDORF, Samuel Thomas				
Mini-motet from	SSAATBB			
Micah SMC		S, Bar	org	Biblical
BIELAWA, Herbert				
A child is born WLP			pno	Dutch carol by J. Roentgen; trans: R.C. Trevelyan
BILLINGS, William				
Shepherd's carol (arr. by Abraham Kaplan) L-G				trad
A virgin unspotted (Judea-- a Christmas carol; edited by Thomas Dunn) ECS				From The Singing Master's Assistant, 1778
Note: The following works for mixed chorus (available only separately) are edited by Oliver Daniel CFP				
The angels' carol	SATBB			from The Psalm Singer's Amusement, 1781
Bethlehem	SAATB			from The Singing Master's Assistant, 1778
The bird	SATBB		pno	from The Suffolk Harmony, 1786. Words by Tate & Brady

Composer, Title and Publisher	Chorus	Solo	Accompaniment	Author of Text
Chester				from The New England Psalm Singer, 1770 and The Singing Master's Assistant
David's lamentation	SATBB			from The Singing Master's Assistant
Fare you well, my friends				from The Continental Harmony, 1794
I heard a great voice	SAATBB			from The Singing Master's Assistant
Lamentation over Boston	SATB or TTBB			from The Singing Master's Assistant
Modern music				from The Psalm Singer's Amusement
Peace be on earth (Retrospect)	SATB or TTBB			from The Singing Master's Assistant
Two Easter anthems 1. Crucifixion				Music in Miniature, Boston, 1779
2. Resurrection				from The Suffolk Harmony

The Christmas music of
  William Billings (edited
  by Gillian Anderson) CTW
  1. Bethlehem: or Christmas
     hymn. LM. (While
     shepherds watched their
     flocks)   The Singing Master's Assistant
  2. Boston. CM. for Christmas,
     hymn 33d (Shepherds rejoice,
     lift up your eyes)   The New England Psalm Singer
  3. Emanuel for Christmas (As
     shepherds in Jewry were
     guarding their sheep)   The Psalm Singer's Amusement
  4. Charleston: an hymn for
     Christmas. CM. Hymn 26.
     (While shepherds watched
     their flocks)   The New England Psalm Singer
  5. Judea (A virgin unspotted, the
     prophet foretold)   The Singing Master's Assistant
  6. Shiloh for Christmas (Methinks   The Suffolk Harmony
     I see an Heav'nly Host)
(Note: above works available only separately;
  for other works by Billings, see under
  "Chorus--Mixed" the work titled: "Po-
  litical & patriotic music of the American
  revolution")

Composer, Title and Publisher	Chorus	Solo	Accompaniment	Author of Text
BINGHAM, Seth				
Perfect through suffering CFP			org or pno	F. A. B.
BINKERD, Gordon				
Christmas day B&H				Christina Rossetti
Institutional canons B&H				from inscriptions
1. The wealth of Illinois				on campus buildings of Univ. of
2. There is in souls				ings of Univ. of
3. To thy happy children				Illinois at Urbana, Ill.
The lamb B&H				William Blake
My soul, there is a country B&H				Henry Vaughan
Never weather-beaten sail B&H				Thomas Campion
Psalm 23 B&H		T	org	from The New English Bible
Quasi modo (introit for Low Sunday) B&H				liturgical
Song of praise and prayer (children's hymn) B&H				William Cowper
To Electra (Set II) B&H (For choruses 1-5, Set I, see 1st Supplement (1971) of Catalog of Concert Music by American Composers, p. 19)				Robert Herrick
6. Ile come to thee in all those shapes				
7. A conjuration, to Electra				
8. The vision of Electra		S, T		
9. Let not thy tombstone	SATBB			
What sweeter music B&H			pno or org	Robert Herrick
BOWMAN, Carl				
Festival of praise (a festival Te Deum) TP			org or 2 trp, 3 trb, tba	liturgical
BROWN, Rayner				
Carol cantata WIM			org	Rayner Brown-- from various trad, folk & liturgical sources
Prelude: Salutation carol	TB			
Scherzo: Sunny bank	children's ch			
Dialogue: The birds		Bar		
Canon: Immortal Babe				
Lullaby: Spanish carol		A		
Intermezzo: In dulci jubilo	children's ch			
Fughetta: Coventry carol				
Arabesque: Patapan				
Epilogue: Greensleeves				

Composer, Title and Publisher	Chorus	Solo	Accompaniment	Author of Text
BROWN, Rex P. Three Christmas carols ECS				
1. Christmas is come!				adapted from an old English carol
2. A carol of humility				Welsh carol; trans: Mrs. K. E. Roberts
3. A carol of praise				Welsh carol; trans: Mrs. K. E. Roberts
BRUBECK, Dave The gates of justice (a cantata) SHAW	T, Bar		org or brass ensemble & perc with opt keyboard improvisation	from Hebrew Bible, The Union Prayer Book of Reform Judaism, speeches of Martin Luther King, Jr., & original texts by Iola Brubeck
BUTLER, Eugene Joy is in the meadow (a contemporary madrigal) TP			pno	anon
Sing we & chant it (in: Choral art) NAK				anon
To night GAL				Joseph Blanco
CACAVAS, John American postlude: only yesterday (arr. by John Constantine) TP			pno	Charles Osgood (inspired by inaugural address of Pres. John F. Kennedy)
CALABRO, Louis The child sleeps EV	SAB			Leontina Calabro
CARNEY, David Selections from Carols new-fashioned ECS			gtr, hp or pno with opt perc	
The Angel Gabriel		T		S. Baring-Gould, alt.
A child is born				Dutch carol; trans: R. C. Trevelyan
CLARK, Keith (Arr.) 'Twas on that dark and doleful night BEL/MIL				Isaac Watts, based on American hymn tune from "Hesperian Harp" (1848)

Composer, Title and Publisher	Chorus	Solo	Accompani- ment	Author of Text
COHN, James				
The terrible people			pno (opt)	Ogden Nash
BEL/MIL				
COLGRASS, Michael				
The earth's a baked apple (a musical celebration in honor of Martin Luther King, jr.) MCA		S, A, T, B	small en- semble or full orch (both R)	Michael Colgrass
CRAWFORD-SEEGER, Ruth				
Chant, 1930 AB		S		vocalise
CUMMINS, Richard				
Psalm of destiny FLAM			org	Dag Hammarskjöld; trans: W. H. Auden & Lief Sjoberg
CUNNINGHAM, Arthur				
Harlem suite TP			pno or orch(R)	Arthur Cunning- ham
A little love		S, B-Bar		
World goin' down		S, A		
Sunday in de evenin'	SA(divisi)			
Lennox		Narr		
Mundy man				
Harlem is my home		S		
(Note: Above available only separately)				
DAVIDSON, Jerry F.				
The word made flesh S-B			org	Biblical
DAVIDSON, Lyle				
Voices of the dark ECS			electronic tape & opt bass instr	Biblical
DAVISON, John				
Communion service unison TP Kyrie. Gloria. Sanctus. Christus. Pascha. Agnus Dei			org	Liturgical Prayer Book Studies XII, Second Service
DELLO JOIO, Norman				
Psalm of peace EBM			org(or pno), hn, trp	Biblical
DEL TREDICI, David				
The last gospel B&H		amplified solo S	amplified solo-rock group of 2 sax, 2 elec- tric gtr & orch(R)	Biblical

Composer, Title and Publisher	Chorus	Solo	Accompaniment	Author of Text
DEUTSCH, Herbert A. Mutima WLP			amplified fl & perc	H. A. Deutsch

1. The creation
    2. The judgment
    3. Mutima--the soul				

DIAMOND, David Warning EV			tabular bells	James Agee

DIEMENTE, Edward
  3-31-70: songs for rock
  group based on March
  31, 1970, issue of the
  Boston Globe (morning
  edition)   SEM
		1 solo-
		ist &
		back-up
		singers
			trp, sax,
			trb, elec gtr,
			perc	

1. The Boston Globe				Edward Diemente
2. Malden Miriam				Rachelle Patter- son, the Boston Globe
3. The Cardinal's am- nesty plea				Cardinal Cushing's Easter message
4. New coats at Filene's				text from ad
5. The Easter egg roll				UPI story
6. Mary Wells				Marian Christy, Globe staff
7. Security is a Mercedes-Benz				text from ad
8. Lucretia Love				Marjory Adams, Globe staff
9. There you have it				Edward Diemente
DIEMER, Emma Lou Outburst of praise TP			pno	Latin hymn; trans: John Dryden
Why so pale and wan? NAK (in: Choral art)				Sir John Suckling
DIERCKS, John And thou shalt love ABP				Biblical

The dove of peace &
  other Early American hymns
  (arr by John Diercks)
  FLAM
	unison		pno or org
			& handbells
				7 hymns originally
				found in the 1835
				hymnal, "Southern
				Harmony Songbook"

DiJULIO, Max A sacred service SF	SSATB		electric gtr or pno	liturgical
DIRKSON, Richard Chanticleer FLAM			org or pno-4 hands	William Austin
I sing the birth FLAM				Ben Jonson
Nowell sing we FLAM				two 15th cent car- ols (c. 1430-1450)

Composer, Title and Publisher	Chorus	Solo	Accompaniment	Author of Text
DROSTE, Doreen The song of wandering Aengus GAL				W. Butler Yeats

DUNFORD, Benjamin (Arr.)
Five anthems on melodies from "The Sacred Harp" (1859 edition) JF
  1. Happy Land
  2. Love the Lord
  3. The Hebrew children
  4. Did Christ o'er sinners weep?
  5. The old ship of Zion
	unison		pno	The Sacred Harp, 1859

DUNHAM, Ervin
"A Markham trilogy"
SHAW
  I. On the gulf of night
  II. The valley
  III. The joy of the hills
(Note: above available only separately)
			cel, hpcd, claviette	Edwin Markham

DUNN, Thomas (Compiler) Carols new-fashioned ECS (a service of lessons & carols) Michael Fink--1st lesson: O come, Emmanuel David Carney--2nd lesson: The angel Gabriel David Carney--3rd lesson: A child is born Karl Korte--4th lesson: Lullay, litel child Michael Fink--5th lesson: What sweeter music Daniel Pinkham--6th lesson: To think of those absent Daniel Pinham--7th lesson: Come, love we god Karl Korte: Make we merë (a secular carol)			gtr, hp or pno with opt perc	Biblical Invitation to Festivity, II, B.M. Addit. MS 14997, Oct. 4, 1500

EARLS, Paul
Trine ECS
  1. The flying geese SA
  2. Psalm CXVII   TB
  3. The song of the stars
		cl		Terry Bringle
				Biblical
				Algonquin

Composer, Title and Publisher	Chorus	Solo	Accompaniment	Author of Text
EDDLEMAN, David				
Continuum MEDP				David Eddleman
EDMUNDS, John				
Clambake on the Potomac L-G			pno	trad - American & English
EFFINGER, Cecil				
Paul of Tarsus (3 episodes in the life of Paul the Apostle) GS		Bar	str & org	Biblical
Spring rain (in: Choral art) NAK				Axton Clark
The St. Luke Christmas story (a sacred cantata) GS		S, A, T, B	org or pno	Biblical
ERB, Donald				
Kyrie TP (see also "Percussion")	divisi		pno, perc, electric tape	liturgical
ERICKSON, Robert				
The end of the mime of Mick, Nick and the Maggies OKM				James Joyce
FELCIANO, Richard				
Benedictio nuptualis ECS	mixed or unison		org	Richard Felciano
A Christmas madrigal ECS			3 hn, 3 trb, tba, glock, timp, cmb, pno	trad, 15th cent.
Glossolalia WLP		Bar	perc, org, tape	Richard Felciano
No one who waits WLP	unison		org	Biblical
Out of sight (the ascension that nobody saw) ECS			org & electronic tape	Biblical
Sic transit ECS	SAB, also for boy's choir		org, electronic tape & light sources	Richard Felciano
Somerset wassail ECS (See also "Chorus--Woman's")				trad English carol
Songs for darkness & light ECS				Biblical
1. I will sing to the Lord	3-part ch of equal voices			
2. My friend had a vineyard		S(or T), A(or B)		
3. Give ear, O heavens	SSA or TTB			
4. As the hind longs for the running	SSA or TTB			

Composer, Title and Publisher	Chorus	Solo	Accompaniment	Author of Text
5. Psalm 150			org	
6. Give thanks to the Lord	unison		org	
7. Antiphon	male voices in unison		org	
8. Benedictus (the canticle of Zachary)	unison		org	
Three-in-one-in-three ECS			org & electronic tape	Biblical
Two hymns to howl by ECS	unison			Allen Ginsberg (excerpts from Sunflower Sutra)
Two public pieces ECS	unison		with electronic sounds	
1. The not-yet flower (a crisis of growth)				Biblical
2. Cosmic festival				Elizabeth Barrett Browning
FERGUSON, Edwin Earle				
There will be stars AMP			pno	Sara Teasdale
FETLER, Paul				
Hosanna AUG			pno or org	liturgical
Jubilate Deo AUG			2 hn, 3 trp, 3 trb	liturgical
Make a joyful noise AUG				Biblical
Noel (the ox & the donkey's carol) AUG	unison or children's choir	S	pno, or org or hpcd, fl, cmb	trad
The words from the cross AUG		Narr	org	New English Bible & Thomas Benson Pollock
FINK, Michael				
Selections from Carols new-fashioned ECS			gtr, hp or pno with opt perc	
1. O come, Emmanuel				Jean Lunn
2. What sweeter music				Robert Herrick
FISSINGER, Edwin				
On a morning mist (in: Choral art) NAK				Leigh Hanes
Three sacred anthems WLP			org	Biblical
1. Anthem to the Trinity (Psalm 8)				
2. Blessed be God (Psalm 19)				
3. We bless the God of Heaven (Psalm 92)				
(Note: Above anthems published separately)				
Witness WLP		Bar		trad spiritual

Composer, Title and Publisher	Chorus	Solo	Accompaniment	Author of Text
FLOYD, Carlisle The martyr (indicative of the passion of the people on the 15th day of April 1865) BEL/MIL			pno, 2 trp, timp, perc	Herman Melville
FOSTER, Stephen (H. Wiley (Hitchcock, Ed.) Minstrel-show songs DCP (Foster's songs for the minstrel shows very much different from his household songs, and this volume presents them as he originally published them--for voice and chorus with piano accompaniment. Along with old favorites like "Camptown races" and "Oh, Susannah" are other sparkling songs like "Alway down South" and "Ring de banjo. "			pno	
FOX, Fred Bec--5 SEM	SSSAAATTTBBB or for 24, 36 or 48 voices		may be performed by 12 instr or combinations of voices & instr	vocalise
FRACKENPOHL, Arthur The dolorous laceration of the cardiac suborganization (in: Choral art) NAK				anon
FREDERICK, Donald A prayer of dedication SMPC			org or orch (R)	adapted from St. Francis
FREED, Arnold From out of a wood B&H Lord! Lord! Lord! (jazz rock) BI			pno or electric org; opt: rhythm & bass gtr & dr	trad; Czech carol Biblical
FURMAN, James Four little foxes OX Speak gently. Walk softly. Go lightly. Step softly.				Lew Sarett
GABURO, Kenneth Terra tremuit WLP				Kenneth Gaburo
GARLICK, Anthony Alleluia SEM			org or pno	liturgical

Composer, Title and Publisher	Chorus	Solo	Accompaniment	Author of Text
The Christmas tribute (a cantata--opt: film strip of Renaissance masterpaintings) FLAM				Biblical
Psalm 90 SEM	SSAATTBB		pno	Biblical
Psalm 100 SEM	SSAATTBB			Biblical
Twelve madrigals SEM	SSATB			
1. Ask me no more				Thomas Carew
2. Nurses song				William Blake
3. Like to the falling of a star				Henry King (17th cent)
4. The rainbow comes and goes				Wm. Wordsworth
5. Go lovely rose				Edmund Waller
6. See the day				John Fletcher
7. To spring				William Blake
8. On a drop of dew				Andrew Marvell
9. Take O take those lips away				Shakespeare
10. Slow, slow, fresh fount				Ben Jonson
11. The cryer				Michael Drayton
12. The cock is crowing				Wm. Wordsworth
GERSCHEFSKI, Edwin				
The Lord's prayer TP (See also "Chorus-Women's")				Biblical
GILLIS, Don				
This is our America BEL/MIL		A or Bar	orch(R) or band(R)	Don Gillis
GOEMANNE, Noel				
Prayer for peace of St. Francis WLM Invocation. Solo (Bar). Chorus. Recitative. Interlude. Chorus		Bar	pno	St. Francis of Assisi
GORE, Richard T.				
Shakespeare's Christmas carol BEL/MIL				Shakespeare (from Hamlet)
GOTTLIEB, Jack				
Kid's calls (a quodlibit) WLP			pno	Jack Gottlieb
Love songs for Sabbath (a service with poetry & dance celebrating the holiness of time) TP Adon Olam (The Lord of all). Alienu: a. Vaanachnu (We bend the knee, worship and give thanks); b. V'hayah Adonai (The Lord shall be king over all the earth). Bar'chu (Blessed be the Lord who is to be blessed). Cantillation chorale:			org & perc	sources cited within the contents

Composer, Title and Publisher	Chorus	Solo	Accompani-ment	Author of Text

half Kaddish (Magnified and
sanctified be the great name).
Haskiveinu (Cause us, O Lord our
God, to lie down in peace).
Kiddush (Sanctification of the
Sabbath over the winecup). L'chah
Dodi (To you beloved...). Mah Tovu
(How goodly are Thy tents, O Jacob...).
Mi Chamochah (Who is like unto you...).
Psalm 96: Shiru Ladonai (Sing to the
Lord a new song...). Silent meditation
(Amidah) (May the words...). Vay'chulu
(The heaven and the earth were finished...).
V'shamru (The children of Israel shall
keep the Sabbath)

GRAVITT, John W.
   The hallelujah mass   SSATBB   electric or   liturgical
      FLAM   acoustic pno;
                                            opt: electric gtr
                                            & c-b, dr

      Kyrie eleison. Sanctus. Agnus Dei.
      Gloria in excelsis

GREEN, Philip
   Let me bring love   youth   A (or T),   pno; also   liturgical
      (Mass of St.   choir   Bar   opt parts for
      Francis) BEL/MIL   gtr, c-b,
                                                perc

      Introit. Kyrie. Gloria.
      Credo. Sanctus. Pater
      noster. Agnus Dei. St.
      Francis prayer. Dismissal

HARRIS, Jerry Weseley
   Flow O my tears (in: anon (16th cent)
      Choral art) NAK
   Like as the culver L-G   Edmund Spenser

HAUFRECHT, Herbert
   Poor Richard's almanack BB   Benjamin Frank-
      1. Reflections on the   lin
         New Year
      2. The world
      3. Early to bed   STB
      4. Dispute among divines
      5. Remark from Richard SAB
      6. Women are books
   (Note: above for sale only
   separately)
   Six songs by Charles Ives   pno
      in choral settings BB
      1. Berceuse   Charles Ives
      2. Nature's way   Charles Ives
      3. The side show   Charles Ives

Composer, Title and Publisher	Chorus	Solo	Accompaniment	Author of Text
4. There is a lane				Harmony T. Ives
5. Those evening bells				Thomas Moore
6. Walking				Charles Ives
(Note: above for sale only separately)				
HEUSSENSTAMM, George				
With rue my heart is laden EV				A. E. Housman
HOFFMAN, Allen				
Madrigals CFP				Kenneth Rexroth
1. Do not pick my rosemary				
2. A gold & silver bird				
3. Once there was a nightingale				
4. Last night I saw in the moon				
HOPSON, Hal				
A Psalm of praise TP			org or pno	Isaac Watts
HOVHANESS, Alan				
Four motets, Op. 246, Nos. 1-4 CFP			org (ad lib)	
1. David wept for slain Absalom	SSATBB			Biblical
2. The word of our God shall stand forever (Armenian benediction)	SSATBB			Biblical
3. Heaven (an echo anthem)				George Herbert
4. A rose tree blossoms	SSATBB			Alan Hovhaness
(Note: above available only separately)				
Lady of light (cantata) CFP		S, Bar	orch(R)	Alan Hovhaness
Symphony No. 12 CFP(R)				
Andante. The Lord is my shepherd (Psalm 23--SATB)				
Bird of dawn. He leadeth me (Psalm 23--SATB).				
IVES, Charles				
Choruses for unison choir (transcribed & edited by Ronald Herder from the original version for solo voice & piano, Seven Songs; see Second Edition (1969), Catalog of Concert Music by American Composers, p. 30) AMP	unison		pno-4 hands	
1. Charlie Rutladge				cowboy ballad
2. Evening				John Milton
3. Walking				Charles Ives

Composer, Title and Publisher	Chorus	Solo	Accompani- ment	Author of Text
Circus band (Alexander Dashnaw, Arr.) PIC (See also "Band")	SSATTBB		pno-4 hands or cham orch(R)	Charles Ives
The new river PIC	high & low voices		cham ensemble	Charles Ives
Psalm 150 (John Kirk- patrick & Gregg Smith, Ed.) TP	4-part treble (or boys voices)		org(opt)	Biblical
Serenity AMP	unison			John Greenleaf Whittier

JENKINS, Gordon

Manhattan tower (a musical narrative) MCA Magical city. The party. New York's my home. Never leave me (Love in a tower)		Narr	pno or orch(R)	Gordon Jenkins

JENKINS, Joseph Willcox

As Joseph was a-walk- ing COL		any solo voice		Appalachian carol
Joseph, dearest Joseph mine COL				trad German carol
Two old British carols COL The boar's head. Balliol carol				trad British carols
A virgin unspotted COL				trad Yorkshire carol

JOHNSON, Gordon

Three Japanese songs EBM 1. The world 2. Tears 3. You		m-S	pno	Kenneth Rexroth

JONES, Robert W.

The coming of wisdom with time EV				W. Butler Yeats
An Irish blessing EV				trad

JONSON, William

Heaven (echo song) GS				George Herbert
Virtue GS				George Herbert

KAY, Ulysses

Parables MCA 1. The old armchair 2. The hell-bound train			cham orch(R)	anon

KENNEDY, John Brodbin

The falling of the leaves B&H			pno	W. Butler Yeats

Composer, Title and Publisher	Chorus	Solo	Accompaniment	Author of Text
KENT, Richard				
Come, fill the cup L-G			improvised rock acc opt	Omar Kháyyám
How sweet the moon- light sleeps L-G				Shakespeare
When icicles hang L-G				Shakespeare
KING, Alvin				
Psalm 47 (o clap your hands, all ye people) AUG		Narr	org, 4 trp, 2 trb, hn, tba	Biblical
KING, Jeffrey				
A wind has blown the rain away B&H			pno	e. e. cummings
KINGSLEY, Gershon				
Four contemporary chorales BI				
1. A lady of valor (an epic rock)			pno or org	Samuel Rosenbaum
2. Shepherd me, Lord			pno with opt gtr & dr	Samuel Rosenbaum
3. My rock (inspired by Psalm 92; arr. by Eric Knight)			pno or org	Bob Larimer
4. Rock, rock, rock (arr. by Eric Knight)			pno or org, opt gtr &/or rhythm	Samuel Rosenbaum
KIRK, Theron				
Choral art (Theron Kirk, Ed.) NAK Note: American composers & their works included in this collec- tion are as follows:				
John Bavicchi: Fly hence, shadows				John Ford (1586- 1639)
John Ness Beck: And in that day from Three prophecies from Isaiah (See under "BECK" for the other two titles)				Biblical
Eugene Butler: Sing we and chant it				anon
Emma Lou Diemer: Why so pale and wan?				Sir John Suckling
Cecil Effinger: Spring rain				Axton Clark
Edwin Fissinger: On a morning mist				Leigh Hanes
Arthur Frackenpohl: The dolorous laceration of the cardiac suborganization			pno	anon
Jerry Weseley Harris: Flow O my tears				anon (16th cent)
Theron Kirk: Laughing song				William Blake
Elie Siegmeister: Heyura, ding, dong, ding!				Elie Siegmeister
Four restoration verses MCA				anon
1. White bird featherless				

Composer, Title and Publisher	Chorus	Solo	Accompani- ment	Author of Text
2. Matthew, Mark, Luke & John				
3. How many miles to Babylon				
4. Monday's child is fair of face				
The jade flute BI			opt fl, perc	text based on Chi- nese classic poems
Noel (a cantata) NAK		Narr	pno with opt brass & timp	Theron Kirk
KORTE, Karl				
Lullay, little child (in: Carols new-fashioned) ECS			gtr, hp, or pno; opt perc	National library of Scotland MS Advo- cates 18.7.21 c. 1372
Make we merĕ (a secular carol) ECS			gtr, hp or pno, opt perc	Invitation to Fes- tivity, II B.M. Addit. MS 14997 Oct 4, 1500
KRANE, David				
Celebration (a liturgical experience) SMPC Kyrie. Gloria. Qui tollis. Agnus Dei. Dona nobis			pno	liturgical
KREUTZ, Robert E.				
I arose (Easter introit based on Psalm 139) WLP			org	Biblical
Let my prayer come like incense (Psalm 141) WLP	2 mixed voices		org	Biblical
LAMB, Gordon				
Aleatory psalm WLP				Biblical
LAMB, John David				
The monotony song L-G			cl	Theodore Roethke
LEE, Dai-Keong				
Canticle of the Pacific COL			orch(R)	based on Vietna- mese children's song, with a theme from "Star Span- gled Banner" and a Buddhist chant from the Sanskrit, "Suddh- arma Pundarika Sut- ra" known as the Lotus Sutra.
LEES, Benjamin				
Visions of poets (dramatic cantata) B&H		S, T	orch(R)	Walt Whitman

Composer, Title and Publisher	Chorus	Solo	Accompaniment	Author of Text
LEKBERG, Sven				
Fragrant the prayer	BB			from the Celtic
The love messengers	BB			from the Celtic
Three peavinations	GS			Leigh McBradd
Pavanne. Moment musical. Counterpoint				
LEWIS, Merrills				
Christmas time at the Pilgrim Inn B&H			fl, finger cmb, tri, glock	Elizabeth Goudge
LIEBERMAN, Frederic				
By the rivers of Babylon ECS				Biblical
LINDSLEY, Charles E. (Ed.)				
Community anthems of early America AMP				
Geneva (1810)	SAB			John Cole
Anthem suitable for Thanksgiving day (1804)	STB, SSB or TTB			William Cooper
Complaint (1808)	STB, SSB or TTB			Oliver Shaw
Ranson (1805)	STB, SSB or TTB			Jeremiah Ingalls
St. Lawrence (1805)	STB, SSB or TTB			Timothy Olmstead
Angel's hymn (1809)				Lewis & Thaddeus Seymour
Billow (1802)				Bartholomew Brown
Charleston (1809)				Azariah Forbes
Duxbury (1810)				Samuel Thomson
Hanover (1805)				Abraham Maxim
Sevens (1803)				Walter Janes
LOCKWOOD, Normand				
Choreographic cantata AUG			org & perc with choreography	Normand Lockwood
I will give thanks with all my heart (Psalm 9) AUG				Biblical
Rejoice in the Lord (Psalm 33) WLP			2 hn, 2 trb, timp or pno	Biblical
LONDON, Edwin				
Three settings of the 23rd Psalm MJQ				Biblical
1. "Ah doynoy rohee loh echsavr..."	SSA			
2. "Domine regit me..."	TTBB			
3. The Lord is my shepherd	SATB			
LUENING, Otto				
Psalm 146 CFP			opt pno or org	Biblical

Composer, Title and Publisher	Chorus	Solo	Accompani- ment	Author of Text
LUNDE, Lawson				
The Beatitudes AB			org	Biblical
Psalm 120 AB				Biblical
LYNN, George				
Clap your hands				Biblical
(Psalm 47) TP				
The Lord is good				Biblical
(Psalm 100) TP				
Praise the Lord	SSAATTBB			Biblical
(Psalm 150) TP				
There is a river			pno or org opt	Biblical
(Psalm 46) TP				
McELHERAN, Brock				
Here comes the avant- garde OX	ch of any type of voices	Narr	pno	Brock McElheran
McKAY, David Phares				
A Colonial requiem GS		S	pno	texts & themes from Colonial period
McLIN, Lena				
Free at last: a tribute to Martin Luther King, Jr. (a cantata) NAK			pno	Lena McLin
MARTINO, Donald				
any one lived in a pretty how town ECS			pno-4 hands	e. e. cummings
MASON, Lowell (H. Wiley Hitchcock, Ed.)				
The Boston Handel and Haydn Society collection, Boston 1822 DCP (Mason influenced the course of 19th cent. American music more than anyone else, partly through a lengthy series of hymn books. This was his first one, a historic collec- tion of works in the then new "scien- tific: ([European-dominated] style of sacred music.")				
MATHEW, David				
Identity OX	for 16 speakers with solo parts or multiples of 16			David Mathew
MECHEM, Kirke				
Forsake me not, O Lord ECS				Biblical
Professor Nontroppo's music dictionary TP				Kirke Mechem

Composer, Title and Publisher	Chorus	Solo	Accompaniment	Author of Text
MERRILL, Marlin				
Let it be forgotten OX (See also "Chorus--Women's")			pno	Sara Teasdale
MEYEROWITZ, Jan				
Ave Maria BB			org	liturgical
How goodly is the house of God BB			org or brass ensemble with org & timp(R)	Biblical
On the land & on the sea BB			pno or org ad lib	Jan Meyerowitz
MILLER, Edward				
The seven last days ECS			perc, 2 stereo tape play-back systems, 16 mm silent film	Donald Justice
MOE, Daniel				
Psalm concertato AUG			brass qrt & c-b	Biblical
Part I (Psalm 150) Part II (Psalm 103) Part III (Psalm 47)				
MURRAY, Bain				
Safe in their alabaster chambers GAL			E-hn, vlc (or org)	Emily Dickinson

MUSIC FOR THE CONTEMPO-
RARY CHOIR, Books 1 & 2 AUG
                    unison
                    & 2-part choir
(Note: These books, each containing
12 songs for young voices, are offered
as an introduction to contemporary
sounds in church music, using original
tunes, chorale melodies and folktunes.
Composers include Robert Leaf, Richard Proulx, Ronald Nelson, Dale Wood,
Philip Young, Austin Lovelace, &
others)

Composer, Title and Publisher	Chorus	Solo	Accompaniment	Author of Text
NAJERA, Edmund				
The nightingale WIM		S, T		trad
NEAR, Gerald				
Come, Thou long-expected Jesus AUG			org	Charles Wesley
Drop, drop, slow tears HWG			org	Phineas Fletcher
Four selections from the mass AUG Kyrie. Gloria. Sanctus. Agnus Dei			org or brass ensemble	liturgical

Composer, Title and Publisher	Chorus	Solo	Accompaniment	Author of Text
NELSON, Ron				
Prayer of Emperor of China on the altar of heaven, Dec. 21, 1539 B&H		Bar	org, winds, brass, perc	Ron Nelson
Thy truth is great B&H			pno or org	Samuel H. Miller
NELSON, Ronald A.				
The passion according to Saint Mark AUG		Narr	org or pno or orch(R)	Biblical
NORDOFF, Paul				
The twenty-third Psalm TP	speaking & singing choruses		pno & bells	Biblical
OAKES, Rodney				
The primrose WLP				Robert Burns
OLIVEROS, Pauline				
Meditation on the points of the compass MEDP			perc	Pauline Oliveros
OLSON, Robert G.				
Christmas Haiku L-G		S, A		Geo. A. Willey
PAPALE, Henry				
Rock a' my soul WLP			cl & Chinese temple blocks	trad Negro spiritual
PARKER, Alice				
Carols to play & sing ECS			hand-bells or chimes, tri, wood-blocks, tam, cmb, t-dr, org	
1. In Bethlehem				Piae Cantiones, 1582; trans: Maurice Bell
2. I saw a stable				Mary E. Coleridge
3. Shrill chanticleer (above available only separately)				William Austin (1587-1633)
An Easter rejoicing ECS			perc, hp, pno & org	
1. Christ the Lord is risen				Isaac Watts (tune: Old German)
2. Earth now is green				Sir J. Davies, 1599
3. Gabriel's message SSA		S		Piae Cantiones; trans: J. M. Neale
4. We are a garden				Isaac Watts (tune: Babylon, 1815)
5. I got me flowers		T		George Herbert
6. Seasons & times				Isaac Watts
7. Like flow'rs we spring up fair	TB			anon, before 1596
8. Drop, drop, slow tears		Bar		Phineas Fletcher, 1633

Composer, Title and Publisher	Chorus	Solo	Accompaniment	Author of Text
9. Most glorious Lord of life				Edmund Spenser, 1595
10. O for a shout of sacred joy				Isaac Watts
11. Christ, my beloved		A		Wm. Baldwin, 1549
12. Jesus, whom every saint adores				Isaac Watts
13. Christ the Lord is risen				Isaac Watts & Henry More
A play on numbers ECS	2-part ch for treble voices		pno	Alice Parker
Twos & fours. Twos & threes. Eights				
A sermon from the mountain (Martin Luther King, Jr.) ECS		S, T, Bar	gtr, dr, str orch	Alice Parker
1. Invitation & response				
2. Blessings				
3. Exhortation & response				
4. The rule & response				
5. The promise & response				
6. The reward & response				
PARKER, Horatio (H. Wiley Hitchcock, Ed.)				
Hora novissima, Op. 30 DCP	SSAATTBB	S, A, T, B	org & orch	De Contemptu Mundi, by Bernard de Morlaix, Latin poet, 12th cent
PARRIS, Robert				
Jesu dulcis memoria CTW				St. Bernard of Clairvaux; trans: Gerard Manley Hopkins
PERERA, Ronald				
The Lord's prayer ECS				Biblical
PFAUTSCH, Lloyd				
The Beatitude of John (a cantata) FLAM			gtr, finger cmb, hand-bells	Biblical
A day for dancing L-G			pno or fl, ob, bsn, perc	trad 14th & 15th cent
The call to the dance. The dance of Eden. The dance of prophecy. The dance of promise. The dance of announcement. The dance of fulfillment. The dance of adoration. The dance of gifts. The eternal dance				
Gloria L-G		m-S	pno or 3 trp, perc	liturgical
Jubilate Deo L-G			org or brass ensemble	Biblical
PINKHAM, Daniel				
Ascension cantata ECS			2 fl, 4 trp, 4 hn, 3 trb,	Biblical
I. Ascendit Deus				

Composer, Title and Publisher	Chorus	Solo	Accompaniment	Author of Text
II. In illo tempore			tba, c-b,	
III. O Rex gloriae			org (ad lib),	
IV. Psallite Domino			timp, perc (parts on rental)	
The call of Isaiah ECS			org & electronic tape, opt perc	Biblical
Come, love we God (in: Carols new-fashioned or available separately) ECS			pno or hp, gtr	collected by Sir Richard Shanne, 1611
Eight Psalm motets CFP				Biblical
1. O Lord God				
2. Why art Thou cast down?				
3. Thou hast loved righteousness				
4. Open to me the gates of righteousness				
5. Behold, how good and how pleasant				
6. How precious is Thy loving kindness				
7. Grace is poured abroad				
8. I have preached righteousness				
(Note: above available only separately)				
Here repose, O broken body GAL				Biblical
The message ECS			gtr & pno	Siegfried Sassoon
Pater noster ECS			org or ob, E-hn, 2 bsn perc (ad lib)	liturgical
Seven choruses from Medea of Euripides (by Virgil Thomson as arr. by Daniel Pinkham) GS (See also: "Chorus--Women's")				Euripides
The seven last words of Christ ECS	T, B-Bar B		org & electronic tape	Biblical
The sheepheards song (a caroll or himme for Christmas ECS	S		opt electronic tape	E.B. (from England's Helicon, 1600)
To think of those absent (in: Carols new-fashioned or available separately) ECS			pno or hp, gtr	Norma Farber
Two verse anthems by Pelham Humphrys (1647-1674) as edited by Daniel Pinkham ECS 1. O Lord my God (Psalm 22) 2. Hear, O heavens	A, T, B		org or str with org continuo	Biblical
POLIFRONE, Jon J. Magnificat AMP			brass ensemble	liturgical
POLITICAL & patriotic music of the American revolution (Gillian Anderson, Ed.) CTW				
1. William Billings--Chester				New England Psalm Singer, 1770 & The Singing Master's Assistant, 1778
2. William Billings--Lamentation over Boston				The Singing Master's Assistant
3. William Billings--Retrospect				The Singing Master's Assistant
4. William Billings--Two American songs: Columbia & Corsica				

Composer, Title and Publisher	Chorus	Solo	Accompani- ment	Author of Text
5. Two loyal songs				
William Billings--Liberty				from the Apollon-
Anon--A loyal song (SAB)				ian Harmony
6. Abraham Wood--Worcester.				Andrew Law: Se-
On peace. Hymn XXXII				lect Harmony, 1779
7. Benjamin West (?)--An anthem (Psalm 124)				Biblical
8. Andrew Law--The American hero				anon
POZDRO, John				
They that go down to the			org	Biblical
sea in ships (Psalm 107) L-G				
PRENTICE, Fred				
Madrisongs TP				trad
1. April is in my mistress' face				
2. I thought that love had been a boy				
3. Grace my lovely one				
My soul doth magnify the Lord TP				Biblical
PROULX, Richard				
The just man shall flourish	unison		fl, ob,	Biblical
(Psalm 92) AUG			org	
RAFFMAN, Relly				
Come be my love BB	SATBB			Christopher Marlowe
Fye on sinful fantasy	SSAATTBB			Shakespeare
BB				
Sonnet XXX BB	SAATB			Shakespeare
RAMSIER, Paul				
Eden GS			pno	Paul Ramsier
Wine (riddle) GS			pno	Paul Ramsier
RAPHLING, Sam				
Fugue on "money" TP			pno	Richard Armour
READ, Gardner				
Come through the field				Auvergne folksong
(Viens par le pré) SEM				
The reveille SEM			2 bsn, 4 hn,	Bret Harte
			4 trp, 4 trb,	
			tba, timp,	
			perc, org	
Song of the spinner				Auvergne folksong
(Chant de fileuse) COL				freely arr. by Gard-
				ner Read with Eng.
				text by Vail Read
REAM, Albert				
The uttermost dawn TP		any solo voice	org	based on a Gaelic melody
RICKARD, Jeffrey				
Gloria AUG				liturgical

Composer, Title and Publisher	Chorus	Solo	Accompaniment	Author of Text
RIEGGER, Wallingford				
The Riegger anthem book (a collection of 10 seasonal & general anthems from many periods & countries.) FLAM	youth or adult choir SAB			
ROREM, Ned				
Canticles (English settings of seven liturgical songs) B&H				liturgical
Set I.				
1. Confitebor tibi		solo or unison		
2. Magnificat anima mea		SA or TB		
3. Nunc dimittis		SAT		
Set II.				
4. Benedictus es Domine				
5. Phos Hilarion				Greek, 3rd cent; trans: N. R.
6. Ecce Deus				
Canticle of the lamb (Note: sets I & II & Canticle available only separately)				
Lift up your heads (The ascension) B&H			org or wind ensemble: 2 fl, 2 ob, 2 cl, 2 hn, 2 bsn, 3 trp, 3 trb, tba, perc	John Beaumont
Miracles of Christmas B&H			org or pno	Ruth A. Jacob
Praises for the nativity B&H				Biblical
Virelai B&H				Chaucer
RUSSELL, Wilbur P. (Arr.)				
Seven introits for the morning service JF O come & sing. Praise the Lord. Mighty God, while the angels bless Thee. Awake, my soul. Praise to the holiest. Come, Holy Ghost. As the sun	unison		org or pno	arr. from hymn tunes found in Southern Harmony 1854
Six closing responses (with tunes from William Walker's "Southern Harmony," 1854) TP	unison with pno or SATB a cappella			
1. Fourth in Thy name (tune: Distress)				Charles Wesley (1707-1788)
2. Jesus, where'er Thy people meet (tune: French broad)				William Cowper (1731-1800)
3. Author of the new creation (tune: Jefferson)				Paulus Gerhardt (1607-1750)

Composer, Title and Publisher	Chorus	Solo	Accompani-ment	Author of Text
4. Lord, Thou has been our dwelling place (Psalm 90) (tune: Portugal)				Biblical
5. Direct, control, suggest this day (tune: Hebron)				Thomas Ken (1637-1711)
6. Christ is the world's redeemer (tune: Complainer)				Columba (521-597); trans: D. Macgregor

SANKY, et al. (H. Wiley Hitchcock, Ed.)
  Gospel hymns nos. 1 to 6 DCP
  (The final cumulation of gospel
  hymnbooks produced from 1875
  on by the spellbinding gospel
  singer-composer of the late
  19th cent)

SARGENT, David
  Nunc sancte nobis MEDP   liturgical

SCHIFRIN, Lalo
  Madrigals for the space   Narr   pno   Ray Bradbury
    age AMP
  I walk in space. Dark rock on
  flint of stone. We search and
  find. The rocket bursts in
  space. A million meteors. We
  drift, we fly. Space! is space
  not curved? Listen! What a
  wonder, what a dread! We move,
  we go, we seek

SCHUMAN, William
  Declaration chorale TP   Walt Whitman
  Mail order madrigals TP   texts freely adapted
    1. Attention ladies!   TBB   from the Sears, Roe-
    2. Superfluous hair   SSAA   buck 1897 catalog
    3. Sweet refreshing sleep
    4. Dr. Worden's pills
  Orpheus & his lute GS   Shakespeare
  (See also "Chorus--Women's")

SCHWARTZ, Paul
  Madrigal BB   Robert Hillyer

SIEGMEISTER, Elie
  Heyura, ding, dong, ding!   Elie Siegmeister
    (in: Choral art) NAK

SKOLNIK, Walter
  Song for all seas, all ships EV   Walt Whitman

Composer, Title and Publisher	Chorus	Solo	Accompaniment	Author of Text

SMITH, Gregg
  Babel GS
   (Multidimensional music)
	mixed ch
	or solo qrt;
	5 speaking groups
			pno-2
			players
				Biblical

SMITH, Julia
  Our heritage (for
    festival occasions)
    (See also "Chorus--Women's")
	SSAATB
	TP
			pno or
			orch(R)
			or band(R)
				Arthur M. Sampley

SMITH, Michael In that day ECS	speaking ch	Bar		Biblical
SMITH, William Ria Sunday TP		S	pno, vib (or any bell or chime-like instr)	William Smith

SOWERBY, Leo
  O God, our help in
    ages past HWG
			org,
			2 trp,
			2 trb,
			timp
				arr from anthem by
				Wm. Croft, 1708;
				text by Isaac Watts

SPENCER, Williametta
  A babe is born (madrigal for Christmas) AMP
  Four madrigals MPC
    1. O cool is the valley
    2. Lean out of the window,
        Goldenhair
    3. Rain has fallen
    4. Who goes amid the green wood?
  Two Christmas madrigals AMP
    Adam lay ybounden. Nowell,
    nowell, out of your sleep
				anon
				
				James Joyce
				
				anon

STEVENS, Halsey
  Hungarian folksongs MF
    Lovely is the forest. In the dark
    earth. In the blackbird's nest
				trad; trans:
				Halsey Stevens

STILL, William Grant
  Christmas in the Western
    world SMPC
	Mixed ch
	or solo qrt
			pno or str
			orch
				trad sources

SUSA, Conrad
  Adam lay in bondage
    (Christmas carol) ECS
  The birds ECS
  Chamber music: six Joyce
    songs ECS
    1. My dove, my beautiful
        one
		
		T, B
			org
			
			org
			pno
				Sloane ms., 15th
				cent anon
				Hilaire Belloc
				James Joyce

Composer, Title and Publisher	Chorus	Solo	Accompaniment	Author of Text
2. He who hath glory lost				
3. I hear an army				
4. O cool is the valley		S, S, A		
5. Lightly come		T, B, B		
6. Strings in the earth & air				
I sing of a maiden ECS			org	Sloane ms., 15th cent anon
The knell ECS			org	George Herbert
A lullaby carol ECS			pno	anon 15th cent, English
Two rock carols ECS			org	Jon L. Peterson
1. Man is born				
2. An elegy carol		Bar		
SWANN, Donald				
Requiem for the living GS		Narr, m-S (or Bar)	perc, cimbalom	Cecil Day Lewis
TAYLOR, Clifford				
23 Psalme of David L-G		A	pno	Biblical
THOMPSON, Randall				
Antiphon ECS				George Herbert
Bitter-sweet ECS				George Herbert
The eternal dove ECS				Joseph Beaumont (1615-1699)
The mirror of St. Anne (an antiphonal setting in inverse contrary imitation) ECS				Isaac Watts
THOMSON, Virgil				
The nativity as sung by the shepherds GS			pno	Richard Crashaw
Seven choruses from the Medea of Euripides (as arr by Daniel Pinkham) GS (See also "Chorus--Women's")			perc (ad lib.)	Euripides
TRACK, Gerhard				
The colors of spring EV				Rosemary Renner
1. I close my eyes SSAA				
2. It has been worth it				
3. The stars are the color of beauty				
4. This is my joy				
5. You are far, my darling TTBB (See also "Chorus--Women's" and "--Men's")				
TURNER, Robert				
Prophetic song PIC	treble ch			Percy B. Shelley
WALKER, George				
Stars AMP		divisi		Susan D. Keeney

Composer, Title and Publisher	Chorus	Solo	Accompaniment	Author of Text
WARD-STEINMAN, David				
The song of Moses GAL		S, 2 T, Bar, Narr	orch(R)	Biblical
WASHBURN, Robert				
Gloria in excelsis OX			pno or org or 3 trp, 2 hn, 3 trb, tba	liturgical
WEBBER, Andrew Lloyd				
Jesus Christ superstar (rock opera) (choral arr by Neil Slater) MCA			amplified gtr, b-gtr, perc	Tim Rice
I don't know how to love Him. I only want to say. Gethsemane. Hosanna. Everything's alright. Superstar. Heaven on their minds				
WEINANDT, Elwyn A. and Robert H. Young, Eds.				
The anthem in England & America, Vol. 1 JF			pno	Biblical
By the rivers of Babylon (Caleb Ashworth--1722-1775)				
Thou wilt keep Him in perfect peace (Dudley Buck--1839-1909)				
Come unto me (Henry Stephen Cutler--1824-1902)				
Hosanna, blessed is he that comes (Christian Gregor--1723-1801)				
Hallelujah to the God of Israel (Franz Joseph Haydn--1732-1809)				
The 23rd Psalm (Francis Hopkinson-- 1737-1791)				
Salvation belongeth unto the Lord (James Kent--1700-1776)				
I will magnify Thee, O God (William Knapp--1698-1768)				
The Lord descended (James Lyon-- 1735-1794)				Sternhold & Hopkins Psalter
O praise the Lord, all ye nations (Lowell Mason--1792-1872)				Biblical
(Note: all above works published only separately)				
WEISGALL, Hugo				
Three Hebraic folksongs TP				
1. So spake Rabbi Akiba				Omar Rabbi Akiba
2. How fair is Thy love				K'felach horimon
3. Fortress, rock of our salvation				Moos Tzur

Composer, Title and Publisher	Chorus	Solo	Accompaniment	Author of Text
WHEAR, Paul				
Joyful--jubilate LMP			perc	both Latin & English speaking & tonal sounds
WHITE, John				
Canticle of brotherhood L-G			org	Biblical
Three madrigals GS				Vachel Lindsay
1. Contraries				
2. Abraham Lincoln walks at midnight (in Springfield, Illinois)				
3. Ode to darkness SSAATTBB			perc	
WIDDOES, Lawrence				
Pied beauty TP			pno	Gerard Manley Hopkins
WIENER, Ivan				
love is more thicker than forget BB				e. e. cummings
WILLSON, Meredith				
Ask not FM	speaking & singing ch	Narr	pno or band	from Inaugural Address of John F. Kennedy
WILSON, Richard				
Home from the range SSAATTBB GS				Stephen Sandy
Light in spring SSAATTBB poplars GS				Stephen Sandy
Soaking GS				Stephen Sandy
(See also "Chorus--Women's")				
WOOLF, Gregory				
A time's passing AMP				John Dryden
WOOLLEN, Russell				
La Corona, a sonnet cycle CTW				John Donne
1. Deign at my hands				
2. Annunciation				
3. Nativitie				
4. Temple				
5. Crucifying		S	perc: cylindrical bell & ratchet	
6. Resurrection				
7. Ascention				
(Note: Above works available only separately)				
WYNER, Yehudi				
Psalm 143 AMP				Biblical

Composer, Title and Publisher	Chorus	Solo	Accompaniment	Author of Text
YANCEY, Thomas				
The song of David FLAM			org	Biblical
YANNATOS, James				
Three settings of				e. e. cummings
e. e. cummings AMP				
1. buffalo bill's	TTBB			
2. the rose	SSAA			
3. in just	SSATB			
YARDUMIAN, Richard				
Anthem: Create in me a				Biblical
clean heart (Psalm 51) EV				
Oratorio: The story of			orch(R) &	Biblical
Abraham EV			audio-visual material	
YOUNG, Gordon				
Hail to Thee, eternal God TP			org	Gordon Young
Voices in praise TP			org	
1. Build thee more stately mansions				Oliver Wendell Holmes
2. Still to our God immortal praise				Gordon Young
3. Come, holy spirit				Isaac Watts
4. A mighty fortress				Martin Luther
5. Lord, hearken and pity				St. Augustine
6. When I survey the wondrous cross				Isaac Watts
7. Praise				Biblical
8. O for a closer walk				William Cowper

CHORUS--WOMEN'S (SSA a cappella unless otherwise indicated)

ADLER, Samuel				
God's promise (arr by composer from the segment Jacob's dream from his opera "The wrestler") OX			org or pno	Biblical
Some laughter, some tears: suite based on Jewish folk sources OX			pno	Samuel Rosenbaum
1. Once I had a great coat	SA			
2. Gone, gone is my sunshine	unison			
3. The fiddler	SA			
4. There's a tree	SA			
5. Tum Balalaika				
6. Come, join in our dance				

Composer, Title and Publisher	Chorus	Solo	Accompaniment	Author of Text
ARGENTO, Dominick				
Tria Carmina Paschalia (Three Latin Easter lyrics) B&H			gtr (or hpcd), hp	
1. In Parasceve Domini: III nocturno				Peter Abelard
2. Veritas veritatum				Benedictbeuren MS
3. Carmen Paschale				Sedulius Scottus
BABBITT, Milton				
Four canons (based on segment of "Birthday canons" by Arnold Schoenberg) BB	SA BB			Milton Babbitt
BACON, Ernst				
Nature ECS			pno	Emily Dickinson
I. The mountain	SA			
II. The gentlest mother		Alto ch or A solo		
III. A spider	SA			
IV. The Arctic flower	SA			
V. With the first arbutus	SA			
VI. There came a day	SA			
VII. A wind like a bugle	SSAA			
VIII. Winter afternoons	SA			
IX. The cricket sang	SA			
X. The sea	SSAA			
BEESON, Jack				
The model housekeeper (9 rounds & canons for women's voices) B&H				Receipts by Elizabeth W. Smith
1. Strawberries as a dentifrice				
2. How to stop the spread of disease & to cure cuts				
3. Plumpening cream for hollow cheeks				
4. Rose lip cream				
5. Love sandwiches				
6. How to tell when lard is hard enough				
7. Vegetable down pillows				
8. Milk to fatten				
9. To plumpen cheeks, and to remove a double chin & other unwanted flesh				
BEVERIDGE, Thomas				
Ave verum corpus ECS				English version by Thomas Beveridge
Felowschipe ECS			pno	Florence Converse

Composer, Title and Publisher	Chorus	Solo	Accompaniment	Author of Text
Songs of praise ECS (13 hymns & responses)	unison or solo voice		pno	
1. Honour and glory				Thomas Beveridge
2. Come, labor on				Jane Laurie Borth-wick
3. Lord, when the sense of Thy sweet grace				Richard Crashaw
4. Easter song				George Herbert
5. Calm soul of all things				Matthew Arnold
6. Prayer under the pressure of violent anguish				Robert Burns
7. O Thou whose pow'r				Boethius; trans: Samuel Johnson
8. A sun-day hymn				Oliver Wendell Holmes
9. O God of earth & altar				G. K. Chesterton
10. Thankfulness				Anne Bradstreet
11. My God and King				George Herbert
12. Trinity Sunday				George Herbert
13. O for a thousand tongues	4 equal voices			Charles Wesley
(See also "Chorus--Men's")				
BINKERD, Gordon				
Feast of St. Francis of Assisi: gradual & alleluia B&H	SA		org	Biblical
Infant joy B&H	SSAA			William Blake
BRADLEY, Ruth				
Prince Toto II (a short cantata) CPI	SSAA	m-S or Bar	pno	Norma Sparlin
Rain CPI			pno	Marie-Louise Esternaux
CRAWFORD, John				
The mad maid's song OX	SSAA		pno	Robert Herrick
To music, to becalm his fevers OX	SSAA			Robert Herrick
DAHL, Ingolf				
A noiseless, patient spider CF			pno	Walt Whitman
DUKE, John				
Three river songs BOS			pno	
1. A farewell in the evening rain				Wei Ying Wu; trans: Witter Bynner
2. On the river Chou				Tu-Fu; verse rendering: Mabel Lorenz Ives
3. The wind & the willow				from 25 Chinese poems; paraphrased by Clifford Bax

Composer, Title and Publisher	Chorus	Solo	Accompaniment	Author of Text
EARLS, Paul				
The flying geese (from <u>Trine</u>) ECS (for contents of the cycle, <u>Trine</u>, see "Chorus--Mixed")	SA		cl	Terry Bringle
FAUTCH, Magdalen				
All creation sing WLP			org	Magdalen Fautch
FELCIANO, Richard				
Christ became obedient for us unto death-- Gradual WLM (See also "Chorus--Men's")				Biblical
The eyes of all look hopefully to You WLP Alleluia. Tract. Paschal alleluia (See also "Chorus--Men's")			org	liturgical
O did he whistle & she did sing ECS	unison: children's ch		2 vln, vlc	Richard Felciano
Rescue me from my enemies O Lord WLM (See also "Chorus--Men's")	SA			Biblical
Sic transit ECS (See also "Chorus-- Mixed")		boys'	org, electronic tape, light sources	liturgical
Somerset wassail ECS (See also "Chorus--Mixed")				trad English carol
Songs of darkness & light ECS (For contents, see "Chorus--Mixed")				Biblical
GEORGE, Earl				
Rearrange a wife's affection L-G			pno	Earl George
GERSCHEFSKI, Edwin				
The Lord's prayer TP (See also "Chorus--Mixed")				Biblical
KENNEDY, John Brodbin				
It's all I have to bring today JF				Emily Dickinson
Lala and la B&H				John Garrigue
The look, the kiss and joy (three madrigals with coda) B&H				Sara Teasdale
Two reflections B&H Lament. Brigand heart				Samuel Menashe
KENT, Richard				
Spring songs WLP 1. New feet within my garden go				Emily Dickinson

Composer, Title and Publisher	Chorus	Solo	Accompaniment	Author of Text
2. A drop fell on the apple tree				
3. A light exists in spring				
LEVY, Martin David				
Alice in wonderland B&H			pno or bsn or vlc	Lewis Carroll
Turtle soup. Little crocodile. Little fishes. Lobster quadrille				
LONDON, Edwin				
"Ah doynoy rohee loh echsavr" (from Three settings of the 23rd Psalm) MJQ				Biblical
Four proverbs AB		S	2 trp, bsn	Biblical
MERRILL, Marlin				
Let it be forgotten OX	SSAA		pno	Sara Teasdale
(See also "Chorus--Mixed")				
MEYEROWITZ, Jan				
On a pallet of straw BB		S	pno	trad carol
MIDDLETON, Robert				
On the nature of beasts ECS Sirens. Owls	SA			De Natura Sirenis from ancient bestiaries
MOLLICONE, Henry				
Five poems of love ECS	SSAA		hp or pno	Emily Dickinson
I held a jewel. I envy seas. A solemn thing it was. Did the harebell lose her girdle. Have you got a brook				
MONACO, Richard				
An Easter carol JF	SA		org	Christina Rossetti
PFAUTSCH, Lloyd				
Annunciation L-G			hp or pno or gtr	Biblical
PINKHAM, Daniel (Arr.)				
Seven choruses from the Medea of Euripides by Virgil Thomson as arr. by Daniel Pinkham. GS	SSAA		perc ad lib	Euripides
(See also "Chorus--Mixed")				
POLIFRONE, Jon				
Summer dawn AMP	SSAA		pno	William Morris
RAMSIER, Paul				
The moon & the sun GS			pno	Paul Ramsier

Composer, Title and Publisher	Chorus	Solo	Accompaniment	Author of Text
READ, Gardner				
Nocturne AMP	SSAA		pno	Frances Frost
SCHOENFIELD, Paul				
A children's game GS			pno-4 hands	Christina Rossetti & P. Schoenfield
SCHUMAN, William				
Orpheus & his lute GS				Shakespeare
Superfluous hair (from Mail order madrigals) TP (See also "Chorus--Mixed")	SSAA			text freely adapted from the Sears, Roebuck 1897 catalog
SMITH, Julia				
Our heritage (for festival occasions) TP (See also "Chorus--Mixed")	SSAA		pno or orch(R) or band(R)	Arthur M. Sampley
SPENCER, Williametta				
In excelsis gloria AMP				ancient Christmas text, ca. 1456
Past three a clock AMP				15th cent London Wat
Tyrley, tyrlow AMP				ancient Christmas text, ca. 1450
THOMPSON, Randall				
Choose something like a star (no. 7 from Frostiana) ECS	SSAA		pno	Robert Frost
The place of the blest (a cantata) ECS			cham orch (R)	Robert Herrick
1. The carol of the rose				
2. The pelican				
3. The place of the blest				
4. Alleluia				
THOMSON, Virgil				
Seven choruses from the Medea of Euripides as arr. by Daniel Pinkham GS (See also "Chorus--Mixed")	SSAA		perc ad lib	Euripides
TRACK, Gerhard				
I close my eyes (from The colors of spring) EV (See also "Chorus--Mixed")	SSAA			Rosemary Renner
Van WERMER, Gordon				
Three songs from Shakespeare NAK				Shakespeare
1. It was a lover & his lass			pno	
2. When that I was a tiny little boy				
3. Take, O take those lips away			pno	

Composer, Title and Publisher	Chorus	Solo	Accompaniment	Author of Text

WEBBER, Andrew Lloyd
  Jesus Christ superstar
    (Rock opera) MCA
  I don't know how to
    love Him.
  I only want to say. Geth-
  semane. Hosanna. Every-
  thing's alright. (arr by
  Neil Slater)
  (See also "Chorus--Mixed")
			amplified
			gtr, b-gtr,
			perc
				Tim Rice

WILSON, Richard
  Light in spring poplars GS
  Soaking GS
  (For both above works,
    see also "Chorus--Mixed")
				Stephen Sandy
				Stephen Sandy

YANNATOS, James
  the rose (from "three SSAA
  settings of e.e. cummings") AMP
  (See also "Chorus--Mixed")
				e. e. cummings

CHORUS--MEN'S (TTBB a cappella unless otherwise indicated)

BEESON, Jack
  Everyman's handyman
    (nine rounds & canons) B&H
    1. To cure a kicking cow
    2. To prevent flies from
         injuring picture frames
    3, 4. Two antidotes:
      Against taking poison
         accidentally
      Against falling to sleep
         in church
    5. To remove moles & warts
    6. Potatoes as paste & pen wipers
    7. To rid yourselves of rats
         without poison
    8. An excellent cement
    9. To revive a chilled pig

Receipts by Eliza-
beth W. Smith
(adapted)

BEVERIDGE, Thomas
  Songs of praise (13 hymns
    & responses) ECS
  (For contents & authors of
    texts, see "Chorus--Women's")

BILLINGS, William (Oliver Daniel, Ed.)
  Lamentation over Boston CFP

from The Singing
Master's Assist-
ant (1778)

Composer, Title and Publisher	Chorus	Solo	Accompaniment	Author of Text
Peace be on earth (Retrospect) CFP (For both works above, see also "Chorus--Mixed")				from The Singing Master's Assistant
BINKERD, Gordon				
Feast of St. Francis of Assisi B&H Gradual & alleluia (See also "Chorus--Women's")	TB		org	St. Francis of Assisi
Let my prayer come like incense B&H	TB		org	Biblical
Songs from "The silver tassie" B&H	TBB		pno	words & melody by Sean O'Casey
There is a garden in her face B&H	TBB			Thomas Campion: The Fourth Book of Ayres, 1610-1612
They lie at rest B&H	TBB		pno	Christina Rossetti
BOYD, Jack				
Mark Twain in eruption L-G			trp or cl	Mark Twain
DOSOO, J. M. T. & Jester Hairston				
No ne li domi (You can't dance with me) BI				in the Adangbe Tribe language of Ghana by the composers
EARLS, Paul				
Psalm CXVII (from Trine) ECS (For contents of the cycle, Trine, see "Chorus--Mixed")	TB		cl	Biblical
FELCIANO, Richard				
Christ became obedient for us unto death-- Gradual WLM (See also "Chorus--Women's")	TTB			Biblical
Double alleluia WLP	unison		org & tape	Biblical
The eyes of all look hopefully to you WLP Alleluia. Tract. Paschal alleluia (See also "Chorus--Women's")	TTB		org	liturgical
Rescue me from my enemies, O Lord-- Gradual WLM (See also "Chorus--Women's")	TB			Biblical
Songs of darkness & light ECS (For contents, see "Chorus--Mixed")				Biblical
HERDER, Ronald				
Requiem II: games of power AMP (See also "Voice Solo" & "Percussion")		m-S	cham ensemble, electronic tape, perc (R)	Giacomo Leopardi; trans: John Heath-Stubbs & Iris Origo

Composer, Title and Publisher	Chorus	Solo	Accompaniment	Author of Text
HEUSSENSTAMM, George Never seek to tell they love WLP				William Blake
KAY, Ulysses Triple set MCA				
1. Ode: To the cuckoo	TB			Michael Bruce
2. Had I a heart	TB			Richard Brinsley Sheridan
3. A toast	TBB			Richard Brinsley Sheridan
KENNEDY, John Brodbin Down by the salley gardens B&H			pno	Wm. Butler Yeats
KENT, Richard Spring songs WLP				Emily Dickinson
LONDON, Edwin "Domine regit me..." (from Three settings of the 23rd Psalm) MJQ (See also "Chorus--Mixed")				Biblical
Enter madmen BCM			instr ad lib	Edwin London
MEYEROWITZ, Jan Ave maris stella (Hail, O star of waters) BB			org or pno or wind ensemble	Jan Meyerowitz
NAJERA, Edmund Kamingaw sa Payag ("How lonely is the night") WIM				from a Filipino folk song
NELSON, Ron Meditation on the syllable OM B&H		Narr (Bar)		James Schevill
SCHUMAN, William Attention ladies! (from "Mail order madrigals") TP (See also "Chorus--Mixed")				text freely adapted from the Sears, Roebuck 1897 catalog
TRACK, Gerhard "You are far, my darling" (from The colors of spring) EV (See also "Chorus--Mixed")				Rosemary Renner
TRIMBLE, Lester Allas, myn hertes queene BB			pno or fl, cl, bsn, vla, vlc(R)	Geoffrey Chaucer

Composer, Title and Publisher	Chorus	Solo	Accompaniment	Author of Text
VINCENT, John Stabat mater MCA		S	pno or org or orch(R)	liturgical
YANNATOS, James buffalo bill's (from "Three settings of e.e. cummings") AMP (See also "Chorus--Mixed")				e. e. cummings

CHORUS WITH INSTRUMENTAL ACCOMPANIMENT
(Including full orchestra, chamber orchestra, string orchestra, band and
 smaller ensembles, and solo instruments)

Composer, Title and Publisher	Chorus	Solos	Accompani- ment	Author of Text	Dura- tion* (min)

AHROLD, Frank
  There was the
    door JF
	SSATTB		2 fl, perc:
			finger cmb,
			tri, gong, vib
				Omar Kháyyám	3

ALBERT, Stephen
  Bacchae (a cere-
    mony in concert) GS(R)
	SATB	Narr	electronic
			gtr, sax &
			orch
				Euripides	

ARGENTO, Dominick
  Tria Carmina Paschalia
    (Three Latin
      Easter lyrics) B&H
    (For contents & authors
  of texts, see "Chorus--Women's")
	SSA		gtr or hpcd,
			hp		

BARBER, Samuel
  The lovers, Op.
    43 GS(R)
	SATB	Bar	full	based on Pablo
				Neruda's "Twenty
				love poems and a
				song of despair";
				trans: Christopher
				Logue & W.S. Mer-
				win
					30

BASSETT, Leslie Collect WLP	SATB		electronic tape	anon	

Moon canticle
    CFP (For contents
     & authors of texts, see
     "Chorus--Mixed
	SATB	Narr	vlc obb		17

BECK, John Ness
  Variants on an
    Irish hymn (Be
    thou my vision) TP(R)
	SATB		full or band	Ancient Irish	4

*Approximate. Duration given only when indicated in score.

Composer, Title and Publisher	Chorus	Solos	Accompani- ment	Author of Text	Dura- tion (min)
BENNETT, Claudia					
Three improvisa- tions MEDP	SATB		cham, 2 pno	Claudia Bennett	
BERNSTEIN, Leonard					
Mass (a theater piece for singers, players & dancers) GS(R) (For contents & authors of texts, see "Chorus--Mixed")	SATB	T	full & electronic tape		100
BOWMAN, Carl					
Festival of praise (a festival Te Deum) TP	SATB		org or 2 trp, 3 trb, tba	liturgical	
BOYD, Jack					
Mark Twain in eruption L-G	TTBB		trp or cl	Mark Twain	
BRUBECK, Dave					
The gates of jus- tice (a cantata) SHAW(R) (For contents & authors of texts, see "Chorus--Mixed")	SATB	T, Bar	brass ensemble & perc with opt pno improvisation		40
CARNEY, David					
Selections from Carols new-fashioned ECS	SATB		gtr, hp or pno with opt perc		
The angel Gabriel		T		S. Baring- Gould, alt	
A child is born				Dutch carol; trans: R.C. Trevelyan	
COLGRASS, Michael					
The earth's a baked apple (a musical celebration in honor of Martin Luther King, Jr.) MCA(R)	SATB	S, A, T, B	small en- semble or full	M. Colgrass	11
CRAWFORD, John					
Psalm 98 OX	TBB		2 trp, 2 trb, tba, pno	Biblical	4.5
CUNNINGHAM, Arthur					
Harlem suite TP(R) (For contents, see "Chorus--Mixed")	SATB	Narr, S, A, B-Bar	full	A. Cunningham	
DAVIDSON, Lyle					
Voices of the dark ECS	SATB		electronic tape & opt bass instr	Biblical	

Composer, Title and Publisher	Chorus	Solos	Accompaniment	Author of Text	Duration (min)
DE LLO JOIO, Norman 　Psalm of peace 　　EBM	SATB		org(or pno), hn, trp	Biblical	16
DEL TREDICI, David 　The last gospel 　　B&H(R)	SATB	S	solo-rock group of 2 sax, 2 electric gtr, with full orch	Biblical	13
DEUTSCH, Herbert A. 　Mutima WLP 　　The creation. The 　　judgement. Mutima-- 　　the soul	SATB		amplified fl & perc	H. A. Deutsch	
DIAMOND, David 　Warning EV	SATB		tabular bells	James Agee	
DIEMENTE, Edward 　3-31-70 SEM 　　(For contents, see 　　"Chorus--Mixed")	SATB	a vocal soloist & back-up singers	trp, sax, trb, electric gtr, perc	issue of <u>Boston</u> <u>Globe</u> (morning ed), March 31, 1970	
DiJULIO, Max 　A sacred serv 　　ice SF	SSATB		electric gtr	liturgical	
DUNHAM, Ervin 　"A Markham tril 　　ogy" SHAW 　　(For contents, see 　　"Chorus--Mixed")	SATB		cel, claviette, hpcd	Edwin Markham	
DUNN, Thomas (Comp.) 　Carols new 　　fashioned ECS 　　(A service of lessons & 　　carols; for contents, see 　　"Chorus--Mixed")	SATB		gtr, hp with perc opt	Biblical	
EARLS, Paul 　Trine ECS 　　(For contents & 　　authors of texts, 　　see "Chorus--Mixed")	SATB, SA, TB		cl		
EFFINGER, Cecil 　Paul of Tarsus 　　(3 episodes in the 　　life of Paul the 　　Apostle) GS(R)	SATB	Bar	str & org	Biblical	

56   Published Concert Music.... 2d Supplement

Composer, Title and Publisher	Chorus	Solos	Accompaniment	Author of Text	Duration (min)
ERB, Donald Kyrie TP		divisi	pno, perc, electronic tape	liturgical	

FELCIANO, Richard
  A Christmas
  madrigal ECS
	SATB		3 hn, 3 trb,
			tba, glock,
			timp, cmb, pno
				trad 15th cent	3

O did he whistle and she did sing ECS	unison children's voices		2 vln, vlc	R. Felciano	3
FETLER, Paul Jubilate Deo AUG	SATB		2 hn, 3 trp, 3 trb	liturgical	
Noel (the ox & the donkey's carol) AUG	unison or S children's choir		fl, cmb	trad	3

FINK, Michael
  Selections from
  Carols new-fashioned
  ECS
	SATB		gtr, hp, opt
			perc		

O come, Emmanuel What sweeter music				Jean Lunn Robert Herrick	

FLOYD, Carlisle
  The martyr (indicative
  of the passion of the
  people on the 15th day
  of April 1865) BEL/MIL
	SATB		pno, 2 trp,
			timp, perc
			(See "Percussion")
				Herman Melville	10

FOX, Fred Bec-5 SEM	SATB divided into 12 solo voices		12 instr or various combi- nations of voices & instr	vocalise	

FREDERICK, Donald
  A prayer of dedi-
  cation SMPC(R)
	SATB		full	adapted from
				St. Francis
					4.5

FREED, Arnold
  Lord! Lord! Lord!
  (jazz-rock) BI
	SATB		electric org,
			rhythm & b-gtr
			& dr
				Biblical	

GILLIS, Don
  This is our
  America BEL/MIL(R)
	SATB	A or
		Bar
			full or band	Don Gillis	12

Composer, Title and Publisher	Chorus	Solos	Accompaniment	Author of Text	Duration (min)
GRAVITT, John W.					
The hallelujah mass FLAM (For contents, see "Chorus--Mixed")	SSATBB		electric or acoustic pno, electric gtr, c-b, dr	liturgical	9
GREEN, Philip					
Let me bring love (the mass of St. Francis) BEL/MIL (For contents, see "Chorus--Mixed")	youth choir	A or T, Bar	gtr, c-b, perc	liturgical	
HERDER, Ronald					
Requiem II: games of power AMP(R) (See also "Voice Solo"; and "Percussion")	TTBB	m-S	2 trp, 2 hn, 3 trb, 2 c-b, pno/cel, perc, electronic tape	Giacomo Leopardi; trans: John Heath-Stubbs & Iris Origo	23
HOVHANESS, Alan					
Lady of light (a cantata) CFP(R)	SATB	S, Bar	full	A. Hovhaness	36
Symphony No. 12 CFP(R) (For contents, see "Chorus--Mixed")	SATB		full	Biblical	
IVES, Charles					
Circus band (arr by Alexander Dashnaw PIC(R)	SSATTB		cham	C. Ives	3
The new river PIC(R)	high & low voices		cham	C. Ives	2
JENKINS, Gordon					
Manhattan tower (a musical narrative) MCA(R) (For contents, see "Chorus--Mixed")	SATB	Narr	full	G. Jenkins	16
KAY, Ulysses					
Parables MCA(R) The old armchair. The hell-bound train	SATB		cham	anon	5
KING, Alvin					
Psalm 47 (O clap your hands) AUG	SATB	Narr	org, 4 trp, 2 trb, hn, tba	Biblical	8

Composer, Title and Publisher	Chorus	Solos	Accompaniment	Author of Text	Duration (min)
KINGSLEY, Gershon					
Four contemporary chorals BI (For contents & authors of texts, see "Chorus--Mixed")	SATB		gtr & dr		4
KIRK, Theron					
The jade flute BI	SATB		fl & perc	Chinese classic poem	3
Noel (a cantata) NAK	SATB	Narr	pno, brass ensemble & timp	T. Kirk	
KORTE, Karl					
Lullay, litel child (in: Carols new-fashioned) ECS	SATB		gtr, hp, opt perc	National library of Scotland MS Advocates 18.7.21 c. 1372	3
Make we merë (a secular carol) ECS	SATB		gtr, hp, opt perc	Invitation to Festivity, II B.M. Addit. MS 14997 Oct. 4, 1500	3
LAMB, John David					
The monotony song L-G	SATB		cl	Theodore Roethke	3
LEE, Dai-Keong					
Canticle of the Pacific COL(R)	SATB		full	Vietnamese ms	15
LEES, Benjamin					
Visions of poets (dramatic cantata) B&H(R)	SATB	S, T	full	Walt Whitman	40
LEVY, Martin David					
Alice in wonderland B&H (For contents, see "Chorus--Women's")	SSA		pno, bsn or vlc	Lewis Carroll	
LEWIS, Merrills					
Christmas time at the Pilgrim Inn B&H	SATB		fl, finger cmb, tri, glock	Elizabeth Goudge	
LOCKWOOD, Normand					
Rejoice in the Lord (Psalm 33) WLP	SATB		2 hn, 2 trb, timp	Biblical	3
LONDON, Edwin					
Four proverbs AB	SSA	S	2 trp, bsn	Biblical	

Composer, Title and Publisher	Chorus	Solos	Accompaniment	Author of Text	Duration (min)
MEYEROWITZ, Jan					
Ave maris stella (Hail, O star of waters) BB(R)	TTBB		wind ensemble	J. Meyerowitz	
How goodly is the house of God BB(R)	SATB		brass ensemble	Biblical	
MILLER, Edward					
The seven last days ECS	SATB		perc, 2 stereo tape playback systems, 16mm silent film	Donald Justice	
MOE, Daniel					
Psalm concertato (Psalms 150, 103, 47) AUG	SATB		brass qrt, c-b	Biblical	
MOLLICONE, Henry					
Five poems of love ECS (For contents, see "Chorus--Women's")	SSAA		hp	Emily Dickinson	
MURRAY, Bain					
Safe in their alabaster chambers GAL	SATB		E-hn, vlc	Emily Dickinson	4
NEAR, Gerald					
Four selections from the mass AUG Kyrie. Gloria. Sanctus. Agnus Dei	SATB		brass ensemble	liturgical	
NELSON, Ron					
Prayer of Emperor of China on the altar of heaven, December 21, 1539 B&H	SATB	Bar	org, winds, brass, perc: picc in quarter tone, gongs, cmb, glass wood chimes, temple blocks, anvil, variety of dr, vib, mar, Chinese bell tree, electric pno	R. Nelson	varies
NELSON, Ronald A.					
The passion according to Saint Mark AUG(R)	SATB	Narr	full	Biblical	50
PAPALE, Henry					
Rock a' my soul WLP	SATB		cl & temple blocks	trad Negro spiritual	2

60

Published Concert Music.... 2d Supplement

Composer, Title and Publisher	Chorus	Solos	Accompaniment	Author of Text	Duration (min)
PARKER, Alice					
Carols to play & sing ECS (For contents & authors, see "Chorus--Mixed")	SATB		hand bells, tri, cmb, t-dr, org, woodblock, tam		
A sermon from the mountain (to Martin Luther King, Jr.) ECS	SATB	S, T, Bar	gtr, dr, str	A. Parker	
PARKER, Horatio (H. Wiley Hitchcock, Ed.)					
Hora novissima, Op. 30 (a cantata) DCP	SSAATTBB	A, S, T, B	full	Bernard de Morlaix, 12th cent	80
PFAUTSCH, Lloyd					
A day for dancing L-G (For contents, see "Chorus--Mixed")	SATB		fl, ob, bsn, perc	various 14th & 15th cent texts	25
Annunciation L-G	SSAA		hp or gtr	Biblical	
The beatitude of John (a cantata) FLAM	SATB		gtr, cmb, handbells	Biblical	
Gloria L-G	SATB	m-S	3 trp, perc	liturgical	
Jubilate Deo L-G	SATB		brass ensemble	Biblical	
PINKHAM, Daniel					
Ascension cantata ECS(R (For contents, see "Chorus--Mixed")	SATB		2 fl, 4 trp, 4 hn, 3 trb, tba, c-b, timp, perc	Biblical	12
Come love we God ECS	SATB		hp, gtr	Sir Richard Shanne, 1611	
O Lord my God (Psalm 22) ECS	SATB	A, T, B	str & org continuo	Biblical	
The message ECS	SATB		gtr	Siegfried Sassoon	3
Pater noster ECS	SATB		ob, E-hn, 2 bsn	liturgical	
To think of those absent (in: Carols new-fashioned) ECS	SATB		hp, gtr	Norma Farber	
POLIFRONE, Jon J.					
Magnificat AMP	SATB		brass ensemble	liturgical	
PROULX, Richard					
The just man shall flourish (Psalm 92) AUG	unison		fl, ob, org	Biblical	

Composer, Title and Publisher	Chorus	Solos	Accompaniment	Author of Text	Duration (min)
READ, Gardner The reveille SEM	SATB		2 bsn, 4 hn, 4 trp, 4 trb, tba, perc, org, timp	Bret Harte	6

ROREM, Ned
  Lift up your heads
  (The ascension)
  B&H(R)
	SATB		2 fl, 2 ob,
			2 cl, 2 bsn,
			2 hn, 3 trp, 3 trb,
			tba, perc
				John Beaumont	4

SMITH, Julia
  Our heritage (for
  festival occasions)
  TP(R)
	SSAATB
	or
	SSAA
			full or band	Arthur M. Sampley	10

SMITH, William Ria Sunday TP	SATB	S	vib (or any bell- or chime- like instr)	W. Smith	

SOWERBY, Leo
  O God, our help
  in ages past HWG
  (arr from anthem by
  Wm. Croft, 1708)
	SATB		org, 2 trp, 2
			trb, timp
				Isaac Watts
				(1719)	

STILL, William Grant
  Christmas in the
  Western world
  SMPC
	SATB or
	mixed qrt
			str	trad	

SWANN, Donald
  Requiem for the
  living GS
	SATB	Narr,
		m-S(or
		Bar)
			cimbalom,
			perc
				Cecil Day Lewis	

TRIMBLE, Lester
  Allas, myn hertes
  queene BB(R)
	TTBB		fl, cl,
			bsn, vla, vlc
				Chaucer	

VINCENT, John
  Stabat mater
  MCA(R)
	TTBB	S	full	liturgical	

WARD-STEINMAN, David
  The song of
  Moses GAL(R)
	SATB	S, 2 T,
		Bar, Narr
			full	Biblical	

WASHBURN, Robert
  Gloria in excel-
  sis OX
	SATB		3 trp, 2 hn,
			3 trb, tba
				liturgical	5

Composer, Title and Publisher	Chorus	Solos	Accompaniment	Author of Text	Duration (min)
WEBBER, Andrew Lloyd					
Jesus Christ superstar (arr by Neil Slater) (For contents, see "Chorus--Mixed") MCA(R)	SATB or SSA		full & rhythm sec of amplified gtr, b-gtr & perc	Tim Rice	varies
WILLSON, Meredith					
Ask not FM(R)	SATB (speaking & singing)	Narr	band	from Inaugural Address of John F. Kennedy	3.5
YARDUMIAN, Richard					
Oratorio: The story of Abraham EV(R)	SATB		full & audio-visual materials	Biblical	90

2. INSTRUMENTAL SOLO

KEYBOARD--PIANO, TWO HANDS (Including harpsichord)

AUSTIN, Larry
Piano set in open style CPE

BARTOW, Nevett
Toccata for piano SHAW

BASSETT, Leslie
Elaborations: four movements for
piano CFP

BAVICCHI, John
Toccata SEM
Trio no. 3 (with two percussion
players) SEM
(See also "Percussion")

BECK, John Ness
Five carol fantasies GS

BEESON, Jack
Fifth piano sonata (1946; rev. 1951;
ed. by John Kirkpatrick) TP

BERNSTEIN, Seymour
Birds: a suite of eight impres-
sionistic studies AMP
The purple finch. The humming
bird. The woodpecker. The sea-
gull. The chickadee. The vulture.
The penguin. The eagle
Concerto ("for our time") AMP(R)
1. Gathering
2. Lament for Vietnam
3. Jubilation

BIALOSKY, Marshall
Five western scenes GAL

BOLCOM, William
12 etudes for piano TP

BROWN, Rayner
Passacaglia for harpsichord &
organ WIM

CHADABE, Joel
3 ways of looking at a square
CPE

COWELL, Henry
Hilarious curtain raiser, & Ri-
tournelle NME
Maestoso NME

CUMMING, Richard
24 preludes B&H

CURRAN, Alvin
First piano piece CPE

DAHL, Ingolf
Sonata pastorale SMPC

de GASTYNE, Serge
Fantasia FER

DETT, R. Nathaniel
The collected piano works, in-
cluding the following suites:
S-B
Magnolia. In the bottoms. En-
chantment. Cinnamon grove.
Tropic winter. Eight Bible
vignettes

DIAMOND, David
A myriologue SMPC

DIEMER, Emma Lou
Seven studies for piano CF
Sound pictures B&H

EHLE, Robert C.
Hypersonde for prepared piano
CF

FAITH, Richard
The dark riders (toccata) SHAW
Five preludes & a nocturne SHAW

Four cameos SHAW
  Waltz. Toccatina. Lullaby. Ron-
  dina
Sonata no. 1 SHAW
Three sonatinas GS
Travels SHAW

FINNEY, Ross Lee
  24 inventions CFP

FLAGELLO, Nicolas
  Electra (with celesta, harp & percussion) MP
  (see also "Percussion")

FULEIHAN, Anis
  Sonata no. 9 SMPC

GOTTSCHALK, Louis Moreau
  Compositions for pianoforte (Ami-
  ram Rigai, Ed.) CHAP
  The banjo. La scintilla. Souvenir de Porto Rico. Morte!!
  Bamboula. Marche funebre.
  Minuit a Seville. Ballade no.
  6. Pasquinade. Tournament
  galop

HARBISON, John
  Parody fantasia MM

HELPS, Robert
  Quartet for piano CFP
  Prelude. Confrontation. Inter-
  mezzo. Postlude

HILLER, Lejaren
  Twelve-tone variations for piano
  1954 TP
  I. Theme
  II. Variations upon individual
      tone rows
  III. Variations on two tone rows
      combined
  IV. Variations upon three tone
      rows combined
  V. Variations upon four & six
      tone rows combined
  Scherzo for piano 1958 TP
  I. Prologue (maestoso)
  II. Scherzo (prestissimo)
  III. Epilogue (maestoso)

HOVHANESS, Alan
  The garden of Adonis: suite for
  flute & piano (or harp) CFP
  Komachi CFP
  Spirit of a willow tree. The sage

of celestial mountain. Rain
harp. Sage ascending the
mountain. Flight of dawn
birds. Rain on Blue Moun-
tain. Moon harp
Toccata & fugue no. 1 CFP

IVES, Charles
  Varied air & variations: study
  no. 2 for ears or aural & men-
  tal exercise!!!
  (edited by John Kirkpatrick &
  Garry Clarke) TP

JOHNSTON, Ben
  Knocking piece for piano interior
  (2 players) CPE

KEATS, Donald
  Piano sonata B&H

KOHN, Karl
  Partita CF

KRAFT, Leo
  Short sonata no. 1 for harpsichord GEN

KUBIK, Gail
  Dance soliloquy TP

LA MONTAINE, John
  Sparklers S-B

LAZAROF, Henri
  Entr'acte AMP
  Textures (with 5 instrumen-
  tal groups) AMP
  3 pieces for harpsichord AMP
  Invenzione. Canzone. Notturno

LEE, Noel
  Sonatine OX

LEES, Benjamin
  Odyssey B&H

LEWIS, Peter Tod
  Sweets for piano TP

LUENING, Otto
  Eight preludes NME

LUNNETTA, Stanley
  Piano music (theatrics required
  of performer) CPE

MAILMAN, Martin
  Martha's Vineyard TP
    Lazy circles. Short parade.
    Breezes. Walk on the beach.
    Invention. Inside and out.
    Sand dance

MARTINO, Donald
  Piano fantasy ECS

MAYER, William
  Trains and things TP
    Distant times, distant places
     1. The aging troubadour
     2. Cold of the moon
    A most important train
    Subway in the sunlight

MECHEM, Kirke
  Whims ECS

MOEVS, Robert
  Phoenix EBM

MOSS, Lawrence
  Four scenes for piano SEM

MUCZYNSKI, Robert
  Seven, Op. 30 GS
  Sonata in F AMP
  Toccata, Op. 15 GS

NEMIROFF, Isaac
  Piece for piano solo MM

OLIVER, Harold S.
  Piano etude CF

PHILLIPS, Burrill
  Piano sonata no. 1 MEDP
  Piano sonata no. 2 MEDP

PILLIN, Boris
  Duo for piano & percussion WIM
  (See also "Percussion")

READ, Gardner
  Sonata da chiesa SEM
    (also available for 2 pianos)
    Intrada. Canzona. Ricercare
  Three satirical sarcasms SEM
  Touch piece SEM

RILEY, Dennis
  Five little movements CFP
  Piano piece no. III CFP
  Six canonic variations CFP

ROCHBERG, George
  Prelude on "Happy Birthday" (for
    almost 2 pianos) TP

ROREM, Ned
  Sonata no. 1 CFP
    (Last movt also published sepa-
    rately under title "Toccata")
  Sonata no. 3 CFP
    (1st & 3rd mov available in
    version for 15 woodwinds that
    comprise 1st & 4th mov of
    "Sinfonia")

ROSS, Walter
  Five dream sequences for piano
    & percussion quartet B&H

RUDHYAR, Dane
  Granites TP
  Three paeans TP

SARRACCO, John
  Timpian fantasy (for timpani &
    piano) AB
  (See also "Percussion")

SCHICKELE, Peter
  Notebook for Betty-Sue Bach TP
    (by P.D.Q. Bach (1807-1742?)
    Gingerly edited by Prof. Peter
    Schickele (S. 13 going on 14)
     I. Allemande left
     II. Corrate
     III. Oh! Courante!
     IV. Two-part contraption
     V. Three-part contraption
     VI. Andre gigue
     VII. Traumarei
     VIII. Capriccio Espagnole for
      Charles III "The reign in
      Spain"
    (With program notes & perform-
    ance note)

SCHLOSS, Julius
  Twelve-tone suite for piano PIC
    Prologue. Scherzo. March. In-
    terlude. Air. Chaconne. Etude.
    Epilogue

SCHMIDT, William
  Vendor's call (with clarinet choir
    acc) WIM

SCHWARTZ, Elliott
  Magic music for orchestra, piano
    & other sounds AB(R)

Music for Prince Albert (with 2
tapes and an assistant) BCM

SESSIONS, Roger
Sonata no. 3 EBM

SIMEONE, Harry
Sonatina SHAW
Toccata. Adagio. Scherzo

SPIES, Claudio
Bagatelle B&H

STARER, Robert
Hexahedron (a figure having 6
faces) MCA
Musingly. Gurglingly. Coolly
but not chillily. Doggedly, mul-
ishly, almost pig-headedly. Phil-
osophically. Frantically

STEVENS, Halsey
Partita for harpsichord (or piano)
PIC
Prelude. Sarabande. Loure.
Rondeau. Sicilienne. Passecaille.
Gigue

STRANG, Gerald
Mirrorrorrim NME

SUBOTNIK, Morton
Prelude no. 4 for piano & electronic sounds MCA

VAUGHAN, Clifford
Six preludes WIM

WAGNER, Joseph
Four landscapes SMPC

WALKER, George
Sonata no. 1 GEN
Sonata no. 2 GAL
Spatials--variations GEN
Spektra GEN

WARD-STEINMAN, David
Latter-day lullabies EBM
Jenna. Matthew. David. Mere-
dith. Karen

WEINER, Stanley
Sonata, Op. 5 MCA

WHITTENBERG, Charles
Three compositions for piano CFP

WUORINEN, Charles
Harpsichord divisions CFP

WYNER, Yehudi
Three short fantasies AMP

ZANINELLI, Luigi
Fantasia EV

KEYBOARD--PIANO, FOUR HANDS
(*One piano; all others 2 pianos)

BEESON, Jack
*Round & round OX
Round & round. Accidents.
First tangle. Simple Simon's
song. Second tangle. Musical
chairs. Round & round

BROWN, Rayner
Concerto for 2 pianos, brass &
percussion WIM
*Variations WIM

CHADABE, Joel
Diversions CPE

CRESTON, Paul
Fantasy (arr by composer from
his "Fantasy for piano & orchestra") GS

DEL TREDICI, David
*Scherzo B&H

DIERCKS, John
*Suite no. 1 MCA
March. Dance. Song. Finale

GOTTSCHALK, Louis Moreau
L'Union in 2-piano score, edited
by Eugene List GS
(See also "Full Symphony with
Solo Instrument or Voice")

HAMPTON, Calvin
Catch-up CFP
(Versions 1 & 2 are for 4 pianos or for tape recorder & 2
pianos)

HANSON, Howard
Fantasy variations on a theme of
youth CF

HAUFRECHT, Herbert
  Square set AMP
    Reel. Clog dance. Jig time

KLEIN, John
  Three dances AMP
    Jig waltz. Stoop dance. Whirl

LAZAROF, Henri
  Intonazione AMP

LUENING, Otto
  The bells of Bellagio
    for 2 or 3 players at 1, 2, or
    3 pianos CFP

MICHALSKY, Donal
  Sonata WIM

PALMER, Robert
  *Sonata for piano four hands PIC

PARCHMAN, Gen
  Elegy SEM

PINKHAM, Daniel
  Concerto for celesta & harpsichord
    soli ECS
    Prelude. Ricercare. Canzona

RAPHLING, Sam
  *Four-hand sonata GEN

READ, Gardner
  Sonata da chiesa SEM
    (also available for one piano,
    2 hands)

KEYBOARD--ACCORDIAN

MICHALSKY, Donal
  Four short pieces WIM
    Musette. Chorale. Fanfare. March
  Variations on "Comment qu'a moy"
    WIM

KEYBOARD--CARILLON

PERSICHETTI, Vincent
  Parables for carillon EV

KEYBOARD--ORGAN

ALBRIGHT, William
  Chorale-partita EV

ARNATT, Ronald
  Fanfare for organ CPH

BARR, John
  How brightly shines the morning
    star (Chorale prelude on a mel-
    ody of Philipp Nicolai--1556-
    1608) HWG

BARTOW, Nevett
  Passacaglia, andante & scherzo
    ostinato SHAW

BLANCHARD, William G.
  Lento (from "Two moods") HWG

BROWN, Rayner
  Chorale prelude, Book I WIM
    (Book II is in preparation)
  Five pieces for organ, harp,
    brass, timpani, percussion
    WIM
    Toccata. Lento. Scherzo. Pas-
    sacaglia. Fugue
  Passacaglia for harpsichord and
    organ WIM
  Sonatinas, vol. 1: nos. 5, 11, 16,
    23 WIM
  Sonatinas, vol. 2: nos. 2, 9:
    (Toccatina, variations, gigue),
    12: (first fugue, second fugue,
    third fugue), 24: (Toccata,
    waltz, lento, fughetta), 26 WIM
  Sonatinas, vol. 3 (in preparation)
    WIM
  Sonata for clarinet & organ WIM
  Sonata for flute & organ WIM

CONELY, James
  18 short pieces & modulations JF

CRESTON, Paul
  Meditations for marimba & organ
    GS

DIEMENTE, Edward
  Hosanna I (with tape) SEM

EDMUNDSON, Garth
  Three organ preludes JF
    Lyric prelude. Rondo. Chorale
    prelude

ELMORE, Robert
  Fantasy on nursery tunes SHAW
    Pop goes the weasel. Three blind
    mice. Twinkle, twinkle little star
  From Mixture IV FLAM
    1. Choral meditation on More-
       cambe
    2. Choral prelude on Lancashire
  Meditation on an old Covenanter's
    tune HWG
  Rhumba TP
  Rhythmic suite TP

FOSS, Lukas
  Etudes for organ (for organist & 2
    assistants) CF

FRICKER, Peter Racine
  Six short pieces AUG
  Toccata--Gladius Domini AUG

GOEMANNE, Noël
  Sortie on Easter hymn: "Jesus
    Christ is risen today" (from
    Lyra Davidica, 1708, altered in
    1749) TP
  Toccata for organ SHAW
  Triptych for organ TP
    Innerpeace. Meditation. Eternal
    joy

GOODMAN, Joseph
  Two dialogues for organ & tape
    HWG

GOTTLIEB, Jack
  Organ music from "Love songs
    for Sabbath" TP
    Prelude. Interlude. Mourner's
    Kaddish. Postlude

HAINES, Edmund
  Slow dance NME

HELD, Wilbur
  Processional on "The king's maj-
    esty" HWG

HILLERT, Richard
  Ricerata for organ CPH

HUDSON, Richard
  Trios for organ (vols. I & II) AUG

HUTCHISON, Warner
  Hymn tune suite (service sonata)
    SHAW

IVES, Charles
  Varied air & variations: study
    No. 2 for ears or aural & men-
    tal exercise!!! (edited by John
    Kirkpatrick & Garry Clarke)
    TP

JONES, Robert W.
  Sonata for worship no. 6 (with
    pre-recorded electronic tape)
    SHAW

KOCH, Paul E.
  Passacaglia on a twelve-tone
    theme JF

LACEY, David T.
  A stately prelude (Passacaglia)
    HWG

LONG, Page C.
  Lenten elegy on "Passion chor-
    ale" BEL/MIL

McKAY, G. Frederick
  Adagietto GAL

MADER, Clarence
  Concerto for organ WIM
  Two monograms WIM

MARTIN, Gilbert
  Two preludes on American hymn
    tunes HWG
    Amazing grace. Nettleton

MOEVS, Robert
  Prelude: B-A-C-H: es ist genug
    HWG

NEAR, Gerald
  Fantasy for organ HWG
  Passacaglia AUG
  Roulade AUG
  Suite AUG
  Toccata for organ AUG
  A triptych of fugues AUG

NICHOLS, Anna Mae
  Three elevations HWG

O'NEAL, Barry
  "Our vines have tender grapes"
    (a pastorale for organ) AMP

OSSEWAARDE, Jack H.
  Improvisation for a requiem HWG

PERERA, Ronald
Reverberations   ECS

PERSICHETTI, Vincent
Parable for organ (parable VI),
Op. 117   EV

PINKHAM, Daniel
The other voices of the trumpet
(with tape)   ECS
When the morning stars sang together (with tape)   ECS

PURVIS, Richard
From Mixture IV   FLAM
1. Passepied for a joyous festival
2. Sarabande for a day of sol-
emnity
3. Veni Creator
A solemn music   HWG
A sylvan idylle   TP
Three fanciful conceits   FLAM
Fête joyeuse. A lamentation of
Jeremiah. Homage à Moscheles
(for pedals alone)

READ, Gardner
Variations on a chromatic ground
S-B

ROBERTS, Myron J.
Five for marimba & organ   HWG
(See also "Percussion")
Sarabande   HWG

SAXTON, Stanley E.
Christmas suite   FLAM
The magi. The shepherds. Glory
to God

SCHMIDT, Warren
Fantasienne & fughetta   ABP

SISLER, Hampson A.
Atonal variations on "Trinity"   HWG

SOWERBY, Leo
Passacaglia   HWG

SPELLER, Frank N.
A triptych of praise & thanksgiving
BEL/MIL
1. Prelude: "For the beauty of
earth"
2. Offertory: "Come ye, thank-
ful people, come"
3. Postlude: "Immortal, invis-
ible"

STARER, Robert
Festive prelude from "Sabbath eve
service"   HWG
Three quiet interludes   MCA
Silent prayer. In memoriam.
Benediction

STEWART, Richard
Prelude for organ & tape   HWG

STOUT, Alan
Three organ chorales   AUG
"Wo soll ich fliehen hin"
"Schmucke dich, O liebe Seele"
"Wer nur den lieben Gott"

THOMAS, Paul Lindsley
Variations on a Welsh hymn tune
"Aberystwyth"   OX

TRACK, Gerhard
Festival prelude & fugue in D-
minor   S-B

TUTHILL, Burnet
Prelude for French horn & organ
TP

VAN APPLEDORN, Mary Jeanne
Sonnet for organ   GAL

VAUGHAN, Clifford
Two voluntaries   WIM

WALTER, Samuel
Prelude on a Scandinavian hymn
tune   HWG

WATSON, Walter
Reflection   OX

WEAVER, John
Toccata   AUG

WILLIAMS, David McK. (Ed.)
The modern anthology, part 1
HWG
BARNES, Edward Shippen:
Prelude & festal hymn
BINGHAM, Seth: Fantasy in C
CLOKEY, Joseph H.: Cantabile
(from symphonic fantasy)
EDMUNDSON, Garth: Toccata
brilliante on "All praise to
Thee"
FRIEDELL, Harold W.: Verses
for the Nunc Dimittis

PALMER, Courtland: Choral
with interludes
SOWERBY, Leo: Prelude on
"Malabar"
The modern anthology, part 2 HWG
BAUMGARTNER, H. Leroy:
Vision
CANDLYN, T. Frederick: Elegy
DICKINSON, Clarence: The joy of
the redeemed
ELMORE, Robert: Chorale pre-
lude on "Seelenbräutigam"
JAMES, Philip: Galarnad
PALMER, Courtland: Prelude &
fugue in F-minor
SOWERBY, Leo: Rhapsody
TITCOMB, Everett: Requiem

WILLS, Arthur
Sonata B&H

WOOD, Hugh
Capriccio BEL/MIL

WUENSCH, Gerhard
Suite for trumpet & organ WIM

WUORINEN, Charles
Into the organ pipes and steeples
NME

WYTON, Alec
Christ in the wilderness: partita on
"Heinlein" HWG
Concert piece for organ & percus-
sion JF
From Mixture IV FLAM
Land of rest
Preludes on contemporary hymns
AUG

YON, Pietro
Canto elegiaco GAL

YOUNG, Gordon
From Mixture IV FLAM
Arabesque
Holiday for the pedals SHAW
Noël joyeux FLAM
Noël preludes FLAM
Perspective FLAM
Prelude on an anthem, "Now let us
all praise God and sing" GAL

YOUNG, Michael
Music for organ and brass (2 trumpets, horn, trombone) AUG

STRING--VIOLIN (with piano unless otherwise indicated)

CURRAN, Alvin
    Thursday afternoon (unacc) CPE

EHLE, Robert C.
    Mordorisund for prepared violin
        CF

FOSTER, Stephen
    The social orchestra (H. Wiley
        Hitchcock, Ed.) DCP
        for violin or flute (a collection
        of popular melodies arranged as
        solos, duets, trios & quartets)

HABER, Louis
    Sonata GEN
    Sonatina GEN
    Suite (unacc) GEN
        Introduction & pavane. Jig. Min-
        uet. Sarabande. Double

HOVHANESS, Alan
    Varak CFP

KOUTZEN, Boris
    Music for violin alone GEN

LADERMAN, Ezra
    Duo for violin & piano OX

LAZAROF, Henri
    Cadence III (with percussion, 2
        players) AMP
        (See also "Percussion")
    Rhapsody AMP

LUENING, Otto
    Meditation (unacc) CFP

MOSS, Lawrence
    Sonata SEM
    Timepiece (with piano & percus-
        sion) FER
        (See also "Percussion")

NEMIROFF, Isaac
    Sonata no. 2 NME

OLIVER, Harold S.
    Sonata for violin & piano CF

PERLMAN, George
    Israeli concertino S-B
        Hora-Hatikvah. Nocturne.
        Fantasie-recitative

PLESKOW, Raoul
    Per vege viene in 2 movements
        MM

READ, Gardner
    Sonata brevis SEM
    Sonoric fantasia no. 2 (1965) TP

ROCHBERG, George
    Caprice variations for unaccom-
        panied violin GAL

ROREM, Ned
    Day music B&H
        1. Wedge & doubles
        2. Pearls
        3. Extreme leisure (or, The
            gallows revisited)
        4. Bats
        5. Billet deux
        6. Another ground
        7. Yellows
        8. A game of chess four centu-
            ries ago
    Night music B&H

SCHWARTZ, Elliott
    Aria No. 2 (with drums) CF

SHIFRIN, Seymour
    Concert piece (unacc) CFP

STEVENS, Halsey
    Sonatina piacevole (with harpsi-
        chord or piano) PIC

SYDEMAN, William
    Concerto da camera no. 2 OKM

TUTHILL, Burnet
    For joy TP

WALKER, George
    Sonata (in one movement) AMP

WATKINS, R. Bedford
    Four burlesques CF

WUORINEN, Charles
    Duo CFP
    The long & the short (unacc) CFP

YANNAY, Yehuda
    Two fragments MEDP

STRING--VIOLA (with piano unless
otherwise indicated)

BABBITT, Milton
    Composition for viola & piano
        CFP

BERRY, Wallace
    Canto lirico CF

BROWN, Rayner
    Chorale prelude: "Aus tiefer Not
        schrei' ich zu dir" WIM

FELDMAN, Morton
    The viola in my life AB
    I. Solo viola & flute, percussion,
        piano, violin, cello
    II. Solo viola & flute, clarinet,
        percussion, piano, violin,
        cello
    III. Viola & piano
        (Note: available separately only)

FINNEY, Ross Lee
    Second sonata CFP
    Sonata in A-minor CFP

FUCHS, Lilian
    Twelve caprices for viola B&H

HANNAY, Roger
    Elegy (with tape) MEDP

IAMMACCONE, Anthony
    Remembrance (or for saxophone)
        TP

LAZAROF, Henri
    Cadence II for viola & tape AMP

PARCHMAN, Gen
    Sonata for viola & percussion SEM
        (See also "Percussion")

PRESSER, William
    Prelude & rondo TP
        (or for alto sax)

READ, Gardner
    Fantasy, Op. 38 AMP

RILEY, Dennis
    Variations III (unacc) CFP

SCHWARTZ, Elliott
    Aria no. 3 (with woodblocks) CF

STEVENS, Halsey
    Suite PIC

SYDEMAN, William
    Concerto da camera OKM
    Music for viola, winds & percus-
        sion OKM

TUTHILL, Burnet
    Sonata SMC

WEINER, Stanley
    Sonata (unacc), Op. 17 MCA

ZEIDMAN, Boris
    Concertino MCA

STRING--CELLO (with piano unless
otherwise indicated)

BASSETT, Leslie
    Music for violoncello & piano
        CFP
    Origin. Invention. Variation.
    Conclusion

BEGLARIAN, Grant
    Of fables, foibles & fancies for
        cello & narrator WIM
        (text: trad. & G. Beglarian)

BERNSTEIN, Leonard
    Two meditations from "Mass"
        (arranged by composer) GS

BROSCH, Barry
    Prolations MEDP

FINNEY, Ross Lee
    Chromatic fantasy in E-major
        CFP

HALL, Richard
  Five epigrams CFP

KORN, Peter Jona
  Sonata, Op. 6 B&H

LAZAROF, Henri
  Cadence I (unacc) AMP

LILIENFELD, Charles
  Romance MEDP

MUCZYNSKI, Robert
  Gallery (suite--unacc) GS
    Prelude. Rainy night. Noonday
    heat. Shanty. Winter houses. Ice
    glare. Black iron. September
    light. End of day
  Sonata, Op. 25 GS

PARCHMAN, Gen
  Sonata SEM

SCHMIDT, William
  Spirituals for cello & percussion
    WIM
  (See also "Percussion")

STOUT, Alan
  Sonata CFP

WUORINEN, Charles
  Adapting to the times CFP
  Violoncello variations (unacc) CFP

STRING--DOUBLE BASS (with piano
unless otherwise indicated)

CHIHARA, Paul
  Logs (for one or more bassist &
    pre-recorded tape & optional
    wind chimes) CFP

COPE, David
  Alternatives CAP

DEAK, Jon
  Color studies for contrabass MEDP

DRUCKMAN, Jacob
  Valentine (unacc) MCA

FREDERICKSON, Thomas
  Canto MEDP

HEUSSENSTAMM, George
  Pentalogue (with 4 pre-recorded
    tape channels) SEM

IATAURO, Michael
  Two pieces for string bass & pi-
    ano GS
    Fantasia. Andante & allegro

KLEIN, Lothar
  4 for 1 (suite for contrabass
    alone) TP

LEWIS, Robert Hall
  Inflections I (unacc) SEM

OLIVEROS, Pauline
  Trio (with flute & percussion)
    MEDP

SCHWARTZ, Elliott
  Dialogue no. 1 (unacc) CF

TAUTENHAHN, Gunther
  Suite for double bass WIM

STRING--GUITAR (with piano unless otherwise indicated)

EASTWOOD, Tom
  Ballad-fantasy GS

HELLERMANN, William
  Four pieces for guitar MEDP

SHAUGHNESSY, Robert
  Duo for flute (or recorder) &
    guitar SEM

STRING--HARP (with piano unless
otherwise indicated)

ALEXANDER, Josef
  Three ludes (pre-, inter-, post-)
    GEN

BERRY, Wallace
  Duo for flute & harp (or piano)
    SMC

BRITAIN, Radie
  Anima divina S-B

DELLO JOIO, Norman
  Bagatelles for harp EBM

HOVHANESS, Alan
  The garden of Adonis: suite for
    flute & harp (or piano) CFP

KESSNER, Daniel
  Sonatina AB

PERSICHETTI, Vincent
  Parable for solo harp (Parable
    VII) EV
      Misterioso. Scherzando. Tran-
      quillo. Brilliante. Conclusivo

SCHIFRIN, Lalo
  Continuum AMP

YANNAY, Yehuda
  Harpist's coloring book MEDP

WOODWIND--FLUTE (with piano unless otherwise indicated)

ADLER, Samuel
  Harobed (also for clarinet) SMC

BERRY, Wallace
  Duo for flute & piano (or harp)
    SMC

BEVERSDORF, Thomas
  Sonata SMC

BROWN, Rayner
  Sonata (with organ) WIM
  Sonata no. 1 WIM

BUDD, Harold
  The edge of August CPE

COPLAND, Aaron
  Duo for flute & piano B&H
  Vocalise (transcribed by composer
    from "Vocalise for high voice
    & piano") B&H

DELLO JOIO, Norman
  Suite: "The developing flutist"
    EBM
  Improviso. Canon. Aria. Scherzo

FOSTER, Stephen
  The social orchestra for flute or
    violin (H. Wiley Hitchcock, Ed.)
    DCP
    (a collection of popular melodies
    arranged as solos, duets, trios
    & quartets)

FRACKENPOHL, Arthur
  Ballad & tango SMC
  Introduction & romp (also for
    marimba or vibraphone) GS

HEIDEN, Bernhard
  Five short pieces SMC

HOVHANESS, Alan
  The garden of Adonis: suite for
    flute & harp (or piano) CFP

KAM, Dennis
  5 phases (unacc) MEDP

KOPP, Frederick
  Portrait of a woman SEM

KORTE, Karl
  Remembrances (with synthesized
    & processed sound) AB

KRAFT, Leo
  Fantasy GEN

KREBS, Stanley
  Siva (unacc) SEM

KUPFERMAN, Meyer
  Quiet piece GEN

LATHAM, William P.
  Suite in Baroque style S-B
    Allemande. Sarabande. Minuet.
    Gigue
  (See also "Band")

LAZAROF, Henri
  Asymptotes for flute & vibra-
    phone AMP
  (See also "Percussion")
  Tempi concertati for flute with
    harp, celeste, harpsichord &
    piano AMP
  (See also "Percussion")

OLIVEROS, Pauline
  Trio (with contrabass & percus-
    sion) MEDP

PARK, Stephen
  Pastorale for flute & string
    quartet SEM

POLIN, Claire
  Sonata (first) SMC
  Structures EV

PYLE, Francis J.
  Sonata SMC

RIEGGER, Wallingford
Suite for flute alone,
Op. 8   TP

RILEY, Edward
Riley's flute melodies
(H. Wiley Hitchcock, Ed.)   DCP

SACCO, P. Peter
Moon is rising   (unacc)   WIM

SHAUGHNESSY, Robert
Bolotowsky (for flute & string
quartet)   SEM
Duo for flute (or recorder) &
guitar   SEM

STOUT, Alan
Music for flute & harpsichord
CFP

STRANGE, Allen
The Doug Meyers' playing flute
(unacc)   MEDP

THORNE, Francis
Sonatina (unacc)   JC

TULL, Fisher
Erato   SMC

TUTHILL, Burnet
Three moods (unacc)   SMC

WEISLING, Raymond
This   MEDP

WILDER, Alec
Sonata no. 2   SF

WILLIS, Richard
Recitative & dance (for flute &
piano or strings)   TP

WUORINEN, Charles
Flute variations II (unacc)   CFP

YARDUMIAN, Richard
Work for flute & strings (untitled)
EV

ZANINELLI, Luigi
Canto (or for clarinet or for
bassoon)   EV

WOODWIND--ENGLISH HORN (with
piano)

TUTHILL, Burnet
A little English   TP

WOODWIND--OBOE (with piano unless otherwise indicated)

BIALOSKY, Marshall
Sonatina   WIM

KENNAN, Kent
Scherzo, aria & fugue   SMC

PERSICHETTI, Vincent
Parable III, Op. 109 (unacc)
EV

SACCO, P. Peter
3 oboe solos (unacc)   WIM
1. Falling leaves
2. North wind
3. Winter thanksgiving

SCHWARTZ, Elliott
Aria no. 5 for oboe & bells   CF

SNYDER, Randall
Three miniatures   WIM

WAGNER, Joseph
Three pastorals   SMPC

WUORINEN, Charles
Composition CFP

WOODWIND--CLARINET (with piano
unless otherwise indicated)

ADLER, Samuel
Harobed (also for flute)   SMC

AUSTIN, Larry
Current CPE

BAVICCHI, John
Sonata no. 2 (unacc)   OX

BERRY, Wallace
Fantasy in 5 statements   CF

BROWN, Rayner
  Double fugue WIM
  Sonata (with organ) WIM

CHESLOCK, Louis
  Descant (unacc) OX

COWELL, Henry
  Six casual developments for clari-
    net & piano TP
  (Developments II, IV, V, VI are
    versions of 4 mov of composer's
    "Suite for woodwind quintet")

DAHL, Ingolf
  Sonata da camera AB

DANKER, Stephen
  3 pieces for bass clarinet & piano
    SEM

DAPOGNY, James
  Six variations MEDP

DRUCKMAN, Jacob
  Animus III for clarinet & tape B&H

DRUMMOND, Dean
  Suite for clarinet WIM

EDDLEMAN, David
  Diversions MEDP

EHLE, Robert C.
  Sundridod for prepared clarinet CF

FINNEY, Ross Lee
  2 acts for 3 players (with percus-
    sion & piano) CFP
  (See also "Percussion")

GARLICK, Antony
  Colloquy for bass clarinet & piano
    SEM

HOVHANESS, Alan
  Lament CFP

IVEY, Jean
  Sonatina (unacc) CF

KARLINS, M. William
  Solo piece with passacaglia for clar-
    inet unaccompanied JBI

KOHN, Karl
  Reflections CF

KOPP, Frederick
  October '55 (with string quartet)
    SEM

LEICHTLING, Alan
  Fantasy piece no. 1 for bass clar-
    inet (unacc) SEM

LEWIS, Robert Hall
  Monophonic III AMP

MacKAY, Harper
  Sonatina WIM

MASON, John
  Tenuto SEM

MOORE, Michael
  Ragtime WIM
  Variations on an Irish theme WIM

NEMIROFF, Isaac
  Three pieces for clarinet alone
    MM

NOON, David
  Sonata (with prepared piano &
    vibraphone) CF

RAYMOND, Lewis
  Design WIM

RICE, Thomas
  Fantasy SEM

RUSSELL, Robert
  Metamorphoses (unacc) GEN
  Pan GEN

SACCO, P. Peter
  The cold mountain (unacc) WIM
  Romance WIM

SCHWARTZ, Elliott
  Aria no. 1 CF
  Dialogue no. 2 for clarinet &
    tape CF
  Options II (unacc) (with percus-
    sion and tape optional) MEDP

SCLATER, James
  Suite for clarinet & piano WIM

SMITH, William O.
  Fancies MJQ
  Mosaic MJQ
  Variants TP

TRAFFORD, Edmund
  Introduction & allegro TP

WEISLING, Raymond
  Essence of ampersand (with percussion) MEDP

WHITE, John
  Variations GAL

ZANINELLI, Luigi
  Canto (or for flute or for bassoon)
  EV

ZONN, Paul
  Revolutions (unacc) MEDP

WOODWIND--SAXOPHONE (with piano
unless otherwise indicated)

BENSON, Warren
  Aeolian song MCA
  Farewell MCA

BIALOSKY, Marshall
  Fantasy scherzo WIM

BROWN, Rayner
  Sonata breve WIM

DIERCKS, John
  Suite TP

IAMMACCONE, Anthony
  Remembrance for alto saxophone
  (or viola) TP

KORTE, Karl
  Dialogue! (with 2-channel tape)
  GAL

KOSTEK, Gregory
  Mini-variations MEDP

KUPFERMAN, Meyer
  Seven inversions (unacc) GEN
    Prelude. Boomerang. Jinks.
    Clockwork. Pelican. Mephisto's
    journey. Conjecture

MUCZYNSKI, Robert
  Sonata GS

MYERS, Robert

Three short pieces ART

PRESSER, William
  Prelude & rondo (or for viola)
  TP

RAYMOND, Lewis
  Design WIM

SKOLNIK, Walter
  Meditation TP
  Sonatina TP

SMITH, Stuart
  A fine old tradition (with electric
  piano, piano & percussion)
  MEDP

WARD, Robert
  An abstract SMC

WILDER, Alec
  Sonata SF

WOODWIND--BASSOON (with piano
unless otherwise indicated)

CHIHARA, Paul
  Branches (with percussion) CFP

de GASTYNE, Serge
  Sonatina FER

PERSICHETTI, Vincent
  Parable (unacc) EV

SACCO, P. Peter
  2 bassoon solos (unacc) WIM
    Night. Mirror

SCHWARTZ, Elliott
  Aria no. 4 for bassoon & tape
  CF
  Trireme SMC

WEINER, Stanley
  Sonata (unacc), Op. 32 MCA

WUORINEN, Charles
  Bassoon variations (with harp &
  timpani) CFP

ZANINELLI, Luigi
  Canto (or for flute or for clarinet) EV

WOODWIND--RECORDER

STERN, Colin
    Sonata (with harpsichord) GAL

BRASS--TRUMPET OR CORNET (with piano unless otherwise indicated)

ALEXANDER, Josef
Burlesque GEN
Fugue GEN

BEVERSDORF, Thomas
Sonata for cornet or trumpet SMC

BODA, John
Sonatina for cornet SMC

CAMPO, Frank
Times WIM
Good times. Hard times (inter-
rupted blues). Time to go

de GASTYNE, Serge
Four musical moments FER

DIEMENTE, Edward
Something else (with electronic
tape) SEM

ERB, Donald
Diversion for two for trumpet &
percussion TP
(See also "Percussion")

FLETCHER, Grant
Little suite CPC

HENDERSON, Robert
Variation movements (1967) (unacc)
WIM

KELLY, Robert
Tune of the toy trumpet TP

KOCH, Frederick
Five "Pops" GEN

KRAFT, William
Encounters III for trumpet & per-
cussion (1 player) WIM
Strategy. Truce of God. Tactics

LUENING, Otto
Introduction & allegro CFP

PINKHAM, Daniel
The other voices of the trumpet
(with organ & tape) ECS

REYNOLDS, Verne
48 etudes (transcribed by composer from "48 etudes for
French horn") GS

SACCO, P. Peter
Trumpet solos (unacc) WIM
Song of war. Farewell. The
great road

SCHWARTZ, Elliott
Music for Napoleon & Beethoven
(with piano & 2 tapes & assistant) BCM

SKOLNIK, Walter
Sonata TP

WILLIS, Richard
Ballad for cornet SMC
Sonatina SMC

WINICK, Steven
Equinoctial points for solo trumpet
(unacc) JBI

WUENSCH, Gerhard
Suite for trumpet & organ WIM

WUORINEN, Charles
Nature's concord CFP

BRASS--FRENCH HORN (with piano
unless otherwise indicated)

ALBERT, Thomas
Permutations MEDP

BEVERSDORF, Thomas
Sonata SMC

HAUGLAND, A. Oscar
  Concertino for horn   CPC

KOHN, Karl
  Encounters   CF
  Variations   CF

LYON, David
  Partita (unacc)   GS

PORTER, Quincy
  Sonata   KING

RAYMOND, Lewis
  Design   WIM

REYNOLDS, Verne
  48 etudes for French horn (also
    transcribed by composer for
    trumpet)   GS
  Sonata   SMC

RUSSELL, Robert
  Sonata for French horn (or trom-
    bone)   GEN

TUTHILL, Burnet
  Prelude (with organ)   TP

WUENSCH, Gerhard
  Lento & vivace   WIM

BRASS--TROMBONE (with piano unless otherwise indicated)

ADLER, Samuel
  Canto II (unacc)   OX

BLATTER, Alfred
  Five sketches   MEDP

COPE, David
  Three pieces (unacc)   CAP

COX, Ronn
  Diachronic (with prepared magnetic
    tape)   CF

De JONG, Conrad
  Anraking (contact) (unacc)   GS

DRUCKMAN, Jacob
  Animus I for trombone & tape
    MCA

ERICKSON, Robert
  Ricercare à 5 (with tape or for
    5 trombones)   SEM

GREEN, George
  Suite for trombone   JBI

MICHALSKY, Donal
  Concertino in re   WIM

PETERS, Mitchell
  Rondo for solo trombone (unacc)
    KSM

RUSSELL, Robert
  Sonata for trombone (or horn)
    GEN

SACCO, P. Peter
  Tuba mirum (unacc)   WIM

SCHWARTZ, Elliott
  Options I (unacc)
    (percussion & tape optional)
    MEDP

BRASS--TUBA (with piano unless
otherwise indicated)

CHILDS, Barney
  Seaview   CPC

FULKERSON, James
  Patterns III   MEDP

KRAFT, William
  Encounters II (unacc)   MCA

McCARTY, Frank
  Color-etudes (unacc)   MEDP

MUCZYNSKI, Robert
  Impromptus (unacc)   GS

PRESSER, William
  Capriccio (with piano or band
    accompaniment)   TP
    (See also "Band")
  Sonatina   TP

REYNOLDS, Verne
  Sonata for tuba & piano   CF

ROTHGARBER, Herbert
  Dialogue TP

STABILE, James
  Sonata WIM

BRASS--EUPHONIUM (with piano)

WHITE, Donald H.
  Lyric suite (with treble clef and
    bass clef parts) GS

3. INSTRUMENTAL ENSEMBLE

STRING--DUOS

FLETCHER, Stanley
  Four violin duets B&H   2 vln
  Sonatina for two violins   2 vln
    B&H

FULEIHAN, Anis
  Duo SMPC   vla, vlc

HALL, Richard
  Suite CFP   vln, vla

KRAEHENBUEHL, David
  Variations AMP   vln, vlc

KUPFERMAN, Meyer
  3 for 2 GEN   vln, vlc

MECHEM, Kirke
  Suite for 2 violins ECS   2 vln

NOON, David
  Duo for 2 violas CF   2 vla

SCHWARTZ, Elliott
  Graffiti CF   vln, vlc

STRING--TRIOS

BROWN, Earle
  Music for violin, cello   vln, vlc,
    & piano TP   pno

BROWN, Rayner
  Sonata WIM   vln, vlc, org

CARTER, Elliott
  Canon for 3 (in   for 3 equal instr.
    memoriam for   voices
    Igor Stravinsky)

DAHL, Ingolf
  Trio SMPC   vln, vlc, pno
    Serenata. Notturno
    I. Rondino cantabile.
    Notturno II. Finale:
    variazini, recitativo
    e coda

DIEMENTE, Edward
  Dimensions I SEM for any 3 instr.

FINNEY, Ross Lee
  Piano trio no. 2 CF pno, vln, vlc

LADERMAN, Ezra
  Trio for piano, vio- pno, vln, vlc
    lin & cello OX

LAZAROF, Henri
  Continuum for string vln, vla, vlc
    trio AB

PARCHMAN, Gen
  Piano trio SEM   pno, vln, vlc

PARK, Stephen
  Gigue SEM   2 vln, pno
  Gymnopoedie SEM 2 vln, pno
  Pavane SEM   2 vln, pno

RILEY, Dennis
  Variations II CFP vln, vla, vlc

WAGNER, Joseph
  Prelude & toccata   hp, vln, pno
    LYRA

WUORINEN, Charles
  Trio CFP   vln, vla, vlc

STRING--QUARTETS (2 vln, vla, vlc
unless otherwise indicated)

BABBITT, Milton
  String quartet no. 3 CFP

BECKER, John J.
  Soundpiece no. 2 (Homage to
    Haydn) NME
  Soundpiece no. 4 (Second
    string quartet) NME

BENSON, Warren
  Capriccio MCA pno, vln, vla, vlc

BLATTER, Alfred
  A study in time and space MEDP

CAGE, John
  String quartet in four parts CFP
    1. Quietly flowing along
    2. Slowly rocking
    3. Nearly stationary
    4. Quodlibit

CARTER, Elliott
  String quartet no. 3 AMP

CHIHARA, Paul
  Driftwood CFP vln, 2 vla, vlc
    (If performed by 2 vln, vla, vlc,
    a vln II facsimile part replacing
    the vla II may be obtained from
    the publisher without charge)

CRUMB, George
  Black angels (Images I--for elec-
    tric string quartet) CFP
    I. Departure
      1. (tutti) Threnody 1: night of
        the electric insects
      2. (trio) Sounds of bones & flutes
      3. (duo) Lost bells
      4. (solo) Cadenza accompagnata
        --devil music
      5. (duo) Danse macabre (Duo
        alternativo: Dies Irae)
    II. Absence
      6. (trio) Pavana lachrymae (Der
        Tod und das Mädchen)
        (solo obbligato: insect sounds)
      7. (tutti) Threnody II: black angels

      8. (trio) Sarabanda de la muerte
        oscura (solo obbligato:
        insect sounds)
      9. (duo) Lost bells (echo) duo
        alternativo: sounds of bones
        & flutes)
    III. Return
      10. (solo) Aria accompagnata:
        God-music
      11. (duo) Ancient voices
      12. (trio) Ancient voices (echo)
      13. (tutti) Threnody III: night of
        the electric insects

de GASTYNE, Serge
  String quartet no. 1 FER

DIAMOND, David
  String quartet no. 9 (in one
    movement) SMPC

DRUCKMAN, Jacob
  String quartet no. 2 (1966) MCA

EBERHARD, Dennis
  Verse varied MEDP

FORTNER, Jack
  String quartet no. 7 AB

FRACKENPOHL, Arthur
  Three short pieces for string
    quartet GS
    Toccata. Arioso. Fughetta

FULEIHAN, Anis
  String quartet no. 5 SMPC

HOVHANESS, Alan
  Four bagatelles CFP

JONES, Charles
  String quartet no. 6 CFP

KIRCHNER, Leon
  Quartet no. 3 for strings & elec-
    tronic tape AMP

PERLE, George
  String quartet no. 5 TP

ROCHBERG, George
  String quartet no. 2 with Soprano
    voice TP (text: from the
    Ninth Duino Elegy of Rainer
    Maria Rilke)

ROREM, Ned
String quartet no. 2   SMPC

WASHBURN, Robert
Serenade for strings   OX
(See also "(Orchestra) String")

WEINBERG, Henry
String quartet no. 2   MCA

WILLIS, Richard
String quartet no. 2   TP

WUORINEN, Charles
String quartet   CFP

YARDUMIAN, Richard
String quartet no. 1 (Cantus animae
et cordis)   EV

STRING--QUINTETS and SEXTETS

BASSETT, Leslie
Sextet for piano &   pno, 2 vln, 2
strings   CFP   vla, vlc

ERB, Donald
Sonata for harpsichord
and string quartet   hpcd, 2 vln,
GAL   vla, vlc

FRACKENPOHL, Arthur
Suite for strings   2 vln, vla, vlc,
GS   c-b

FULEIHAN, Anis
Quintet for piano &   pno, 2 vln, vla,
strings   B&H   vlc

STRING--WITH VOICE, WINDS and/
or PERCUSSION

ALBRIGHT, William
Danse macabre   fl, cl, vln, vlc,
BCM   pno

ALEXANDER, Josef
Three inventions for two
instruments   GEN   ob, vla

ASHLEY, Robert
Crazy Horse (sym-   20 or more
phony)   CPE   wind, string
   or other sus-
   taining instr.
In memoriam: Este-   4 players
ban Gómez   CPE
In memoriam: John   3 players
Smith (concerto)
with assistants   CPE
Trios (white on white)   3 trios for any
CPE   players

ATHEY, Ralph
Kaolin   MEDP   any mixed ensemble of winds
   &/or strings

BEERMAN, Burton
Mixtures   MEDP   voices, fl, cl,
   hn, vln, tape

BERRY, Wallace
Duo for flute &   fl, hp (or pno)
harp   SMC

BEVERSDORF, Thomas
Divertimento da   fl(picc), ob(E-
camera   GS   hn), c-b, hpcd

BOATWRIGHT, Howard
Serenade   OX   cl, hn, vln, vlc

BOLCOM, William
Duets for quintet   fl, cl, vln, vlc,
(a farce for fun)   pno, stage mgr
BCM   for lights
Whisper moon   fl, cl, vln, vlc,
BCM   pno

BROWN, Earle
Event-synergy II   instr. varies
TP

BROWN, Rayner
Five pieces   WIM   org, hp, 4 trp,
   4 hn, 4 trb,
   bar, tba, timp,
   perc (2 players)
Toccata. Lento. Scherzo. Passacaglia. Fugue

BUDD, Harold
III for double en-   jazz trio: trp,
semble   CPE   c-b, dr; quartet:
   fl, cl, vlc, vib

CAGAN, Steven
  Divertissement: suite   fl, ob, cl,
    for the dance SMPC   bsn, trp, trb,
                         vlc, c-b, perc
                         I & II

CARTER, Elliott
  Canon for 3 (in me-   for 3 equal instr
    moriam for Igor   voices
    Stravinsky) AMP
  Pastoral NME   pno, vla, E-hn
                         (or cl)

CHADABE, Joel
  Prelude to Naples   fl, cl, pno, vlc
    CPE

CHILDS, Barney
  Any five CPE   unspec combina-
                         tion of 5 winds,
                         strings, perc,
                         &/or voice
  Jack's new bag   fl, trp, trb, pno
    CPE   (2 players), perc
                         (2 players), vla,
                         vlc, c-b
  (See also "Percussion")
  Music for... AMP   four mov: 2 for
                         unspec instr; 1
                         for b-dr; 1 for
                         ob

COPE, David
  Towers MEDP   for unspec mixed
                         instr ensemble

CRUMB, George
  Ancient voices of   S, boy-S, ob,
    children CFP   man, hp, elec-
    (for contents,   tric pno, perc
    see "(Voice)   (based on texts
    Solo")   by García Lorca
  Eleven echoes of   vln, fl, cl, pno
    autumn, 1965 CFP
    1. Fantastico
    2. Languidamente
    3. Prestissimo
    4. Con bravura
    5. Cadenza I (flute)
    6. Cadenza II (violin)
    7. Cadenza III (clarinet)
    8. Feroce, violento
    9. Serenamente, quasi lontano
    10. Senza misura
    11. Adagio ("like a prayer")

CURRAN, Alvin
  home-made CPE   fl, S, c-b, perc

CUSTER, Arthur
  Permutations JC   vln, vlc, cl

De JONG, Conrad
  Fun & games   solo woodwinds
    MEDP   with brass or
                         strings, pno

DEL TREDICI, David
  Night conjure   S(or m-S or
    verse B&H   counter T): text:
    (See also   James Joyce;
    "(Voice) Solo")   with wind septet
                         & str qrt

DIAMOND, David
  Quintet SMPC   fl, vla, vln, vlc,
                         pno

DIEMENTE, Edward
  Dimensions I SEM for any 3 instr

DINERSTEIN, Norman
  Four settings for   S, str qrt; text:
    spr & str qrt   Emily Dickinson
    (For contents,
    see "(Voice) Solo")

DORAN, Matt
  Andante & allegro   fl, vlc, pno
    WIM
  Prelude & scherzo   ob, cl, bsn, vla
    WIM

DRUCKMAN, Jacob
  Incenters for 13   fl, cl, bsn, hn,
    instruments   trp, trb, org,
    MCA   pno, perc, vln,
                         vla, vlc, c-b

EHLE, Robert C.
  Estrangeon for   pno, vln, cl, perc
    prepared instru-
    ments CF

ERB, Donald
  Souvenir TP   a multi-media
                         work for mixed
                         instr, abstract
                         slides, dancers
                         & tape

FELDMAN, Morton
  Madame Press   for 13 mixed instr
    died last week at
    ninety TP
  The viola in my life
    AB

I.   solo vla; fl, perc, pno, vln, vlc
II. solo vla; fl, cl, perc, pno, vln,
     vlc
III. solo vla & pno
(Note: Above available only sepa-
rately)

FRACKENPOHL, Arthur
Suite GS   trp, str

GARLICK, Antony
Duo SEM   fl, vla

GILMORE, Frank
Duo SEM   fl, vla

GIRON, Arsenio
Quartet CF   fl, cl, vla, pno
Vias CF   fl, cl, vlc, pno,
                             perc

GOLZ, Walter
For flute & muted   fl, str qrt
string quartet SEM

HABER, Louis
Parade, blues &   fl, vln, pno
allegro GEN

HAIEFF, Alexei
Dance suite (the   fl, bsn, trp, pno,
princess Zondilda   vln, vlc
& her entourage) CFP

HAMM, Charles
Round MEDP   unspec mixed
                     ensemble

HARBISON, John
Four preludes (from fl, vln
December Music)
MM

HEISS, John
Quartet (1971)   fl, cl, vlc, pno
BCM

HENRY, Otto
Omnibus I MEDP   unspec mixed
                     ensemble

HERDER, Ronald
Requiem II: games   m-S solo, men's
of power AMP   ch, 2 trp, 2 hn,
(See also "(Voice)   3 trb, 2 c-b,
Solo," "Chorus   pno/cel, perc,
Men's"; & "Per-   electronic tape
cussion")   (R) text: Gia-

como Leopardi;
trans: John Heath-
Stubbs & Iris
Origo

HEUSSENSTAMM, George
Music for 3   amplified c-b,
SEM   fl, vib, perc
Trio SEM   cl, vln, vlc

HOVHANESS, Alan
Canticle, Op.   S, ob, xy, cel,
115 CFP   hp, str
(for contents, see
"(Voice) Solo")
The garden of   fl, hp or pno
Adonis: suite for
flute & harp (or
piano) CFP
Saturn CFP   S, cl, pno -text:
                     A. Hovhaness
(For contents, see
"(Voice) Solo")

HUSTON, Scott
Idioms GEN   vln, cl, hn

IVES, Charles
The rainbow (an-   fl, basset or E-
dante con spir-   hn, str, pno
ito) PIC
Scherzo (All the   cl (or fl), vln,
way around and   bugle (or trp),
back) PIC   middle bells (or
                     hn), 2 pno (or 1
                     pno)

JOSEPHS, Wilfred
Octet, Op. 43   instr NA
for strings &
winds BB

KARLINS, M. Williams
Birthday music   fl, c-b
no II MEDP
Graphic mobile   3 or more instr
MEDP

KERR, Harrison
Notations on a   voice, cl, str
sensitized   qrt, pno
plate NME

KOHN, Karl
Introductions &   cl, hn, bsn, pno,
parodies CF   str qrt

KOPP, Frederick
October '55 SEM   cl, str qrt

KORTE, Karl
Gestures EV   mixed winds,
                   electric c-b, pno,
                   perc
Rondino JBI   ob, vln

KUPFERMAN, Meyer
Three for two GEN   vln, cl

LADERMAN, Ezra
Double helix OX   fl, ob, str qrt
                    (R) or str orch
                    (R)
A single voice OX ob & str qrt (R)
                    or str orch (R)

LAUFER, Edward
Variations for 7   fl, cl, bsn, trp,
  instruments VAL   vln, vlc, pno

LAZAROF, Henri
Tempi concertati   fl, hp, cel, hpcd,
  AMP   pno
Textures AMP   solo pno with 5 instr
                    groups as follows:
                    1--fl, vln, ob, vla,
                       cl
                    2--trp, trb, perc
                       1 & 2
                    3--fl, vln, E-hn,
                       cl, vlc
                    4--trp, trb, perc
                       3 & 4
                    5--2 hn, tba, c-b
                    also with hp, cel,
                    harmonium

LINN, Robert
Concertino for vio-   solo vln; 2 ob,
  lin & wind octet   2 cl, 2 bsn, 2 hn
  WIM

LUENING, Otto
Lyric scene CFP   fl, 2 vln, vla,
                    vlc, c-b (ad lib)
Short fantasy GAL vln, hn

LUTI, Vincent F.
Mixed quintet BCM 2 fl, 2 cl, vln,
                    vla, vlc, pno,
                    tape
  Invention. Toccata.
  Theme & cadenza.Chorale

McCARTY, Frank

Trio   ART   sax, bsn, vlc

MacKAY, Harper
Six minutes for fl, cl, bsn, vln,
  six pieces   vla, vlc
  WIM

MOSS, Lawrence
Patterns SEM   fl, cl, vla, pno
Windows SEM   fl, cl, c-b

MUCZYNSKI, Robert
Fantasy trio   cl, vlc, pno
  GS

NOON, David
Labyrinth (a   fl/picc, cl, bsn, ob,
  ballet in 1   2 trp, hn, trb, tba,
  scene) CF   2 vln, vla, vlc, c-b

OLIVEROS, Pauline
Trio for flute,   fl, perc, c-b
  percussion &
  string bass MEDP

PARK, Stephen
Pastorale SEM   fl, str qrt

PHIFER, Larry
Construction no.   3 to 6 instr
  2 MEDP

POWELL, Morgan
Three poems   2 vln, S
  MEDP

PRESSER, William
Passacaglia   cl, hn, vln, vla,
  SEM   vlc
Serenade SEM fl, vla
3 duets TP   trp, c-b

RECK, David
Blues & screamer fl (picc), har-
  CPE   monium, sax, c-b,
                 perc set & film

REYNOLDS, Roger
Traces CFP   fl, pno, vlc, 6
               channels of taped
               sound, signal gen-
               erator, ring modu-
               lator

REYNOLDS, Verne
Concertare II   trp, 2 vln, vla,
  CF   vlc, c-b

RILEY, Dennis
Five songs on   S, cl, vln, vlc
  Haiku texts   CFP

ROCHBERG, George
String quartet no.   S (text: from the
  2 with Soprano   Ninth Duino Ele-
  voice   TP   gy of Rainer Ma-
     ria Rilke), str
     qrt

SCHUMACHER, Stanley
Symmetries   fl(or vln), sax,
  MEDP   cl (or vla), bsn,
     cl (or trb), c-b

SCHWARTZ, Elliott
Concert piece for   fl, ob, cl, bsn,
  10 players   AB   hn, vln, vla,
     vlc, c-b, perc
Miniconcerto   CF   fl, ob, vln, vla,
     vlc
Septet   AB   for 5 instr, pno,
     speaker/singer
Signals   MEDP   trb, c-b
Trio   CF   fl, vlc, pno

SHAUGHNESSY, Robert
Bolotowsky   SEM   fl, str qrt
Duo   SEM   fl (or rec), gtr

SIMONS, Netty
Design groups II   duo for any 2
  TP   instr of high &
     low registers

SMIT, Leo
Quintet   CFP   fl, vln, vla, vlc,
     hp
Suite   CFP   ob, vlc
Trio   CFP   cl, vla, pno

SMITH, William O.
Suite   OX   vln, cl

SYDEMAN, William
Music for viola,   vla, winds, perc
  winds & percussion   OKM
  (See also "(Instr Solo) String--
  Viola"; & "Percussion")

UDOW, Michael
Understanding   6 unspec instr,
  MEDP   8 parade drum-
     mers, tape re-
     corder

WIDDOES, Lawrence
From a time of   fl, cl, vln, vlc,
  snow   BCM   pno

WILLIS, Richard
Recitative &   fl, str(R)
  & dance   TP

WILSON, George Balch
Concatenations   fl, cl, b-cl, hn,
  for 12 instru-   trp, trb, traps,
  ments (1969)   acc, gtr, vln, vlc
  TP (R)   c-b

WOLFF, Christian
Edges   CFP   unspec mixed en-
     semble
Electric spring   rec (T&A)--1
  II   CFP   player, electric
     gtr, electric bass
     gtr, trb

WUORINEN, Charles
Bassoon vari-   bsn, hp, timp
  ations   CFP
Canzona (to the   fl, ob (E-hn), cl,
  memory of   bsn, trp, vln, vla,
  Igro Stravin-   vlc, c-b, vib, hp,
  sky) for 12   pno
  instruments   CFP(R)
Chamber con-   solo vlc; fl, ob, cl,
  certo for   bsn, vln, vla, perc
  cello & 10   (2 players), c-b,
  players   pno
  CFP(R)
Chamber con-   solo fl; gtr, hp,
  certo for   hpcd, perc (4
  flute & 10   players), cel, pno,
  players   c-b
  CFP(R)
Chamber con-   solo ob; tba, hp,
  certo for   timp, perc (5
  oboe & 10   players), pno, c-b
  players
  (CFP(R)
Composition for   solo vln; 2 ob, 2
  violin & 10   hn, 2 trb, b-cl,
  instruments   c-b, perc, pno
  CFP(R)
Second trio   fl, vlc, pno
  CFP

YANNAY, Yehuda
  PreFix--Fix--   bsn, hn, vlc
    sufFix MEDP

YARDUMIAN, Richard
  Work for flute &   fl, str(R)
    strings (untitled)
    EV

WOODWIND--DUOS

BAVICCHI, John
  Five dialogues OX 2 cl

BLANK, Allan
  Four bagatelles   ob, cl
  OKM

BROWN, Rayner
  Symbols WIM   2 cl

CAGE, John
  3 pieces for 2   2 fl
  flutes CFP

CHIHARA, Paul
  Branches CFP   2 bsn, perc (1
                      player)
  (See also "Percussion")

CLARKE, Henry Leland
  A game that two   fl, cl
  can play WIM

CORTÉS, Ramiro
  Duo for flute &   fl, ob (or E-hn)
  oboe EV
  Fantasy. Invention. Elegy. Recitative. Finale

GHENT, Emmanuel
  Two duos for flute fl (or ob), cl
  (or oboe) & clari-
  net OX
  Natasha. Pygmalion & Galatea

GRUNDMAN, Clare
  Puppets B&H   2 cl

HARBISON, John
  Four preludes   fl, fl/ob/cl
  (from December
  Music) MM

HAUBIEL, Charles
  Pastoral WIM   ob, bsn

HEUSSENSTAMM, George
  Ambages SEM   fl, cl

Eight short   2 cl
  duets WIM

KREBS, Stanley
  Contemplation 2 fl
  SEM

LAMB, John David
  Six barefoot   2 sax
  dances MM

LEVY, Frank
  Divertimento   cl, bsn
  SEM

PERSICHETTI, Vincent
  Serenade no. 9 S & A rec
  EV

PRESSER, William
  Seven bassoon 2 bsn
  duets TP

RUSSELL, Robert
  Duo GEN   fl, cl

SCHWARTZ, Elliott
  Ninas CF   fl, ob, tape
  Sibling suite   2 fl
  MEDP

STEVENS, Halsey
  Five duos PIC fl, cl

WAXMAN, Donald
  Duo sonatina   2 rec
  GAL

WUORINEN, Charles
  Bicinium CFP 2 ob

WOODWIND--TRIOS

BIGGS, John
  Tré canzoni WIM 3 cl

BROWN, Rayner
  Fugue for 3 saxo- 3 sax
    phones WIM

CACAVAS, John
  Shimmering flutes 3 fl
    (with band acc)
    SMC

CAMPO, Frank
  Concertino WIM 3 cl

CARTER, Elliott
  Canon for 3 (In for equal instr
    memoriam voices
    for Igor Stra-
    vinsky) AMP

DIEMENTE, Edward
  Dimensions I for any 3 instr
    SEM

HABASH, John Mitri
  Adagio & rondo fl, cl, bsn
    BI

KORTE, Karl
  Remembrances fl (alto, so-
    EV prano & picc) &
      synthesized &
      processed sound

McKAY, Francis H.
  Lyric poem CLB 3 fl

MASON, John
  Canonic device 3 cl, bsn
    SEM

MECHEM, Kirke
  Trio ECS ob, cl, bsn

SCLATER, James
  Trio WIM fl, cl, bsn

SHAPERO, Harold
  Three pieces for unspec winds
    for three
    pieces SMPC

TUSTIN, Whitney
  Pastorale mod- fl, ob, cl
    erne CLB
  Scherzo CLB fl, ob, cl
  Tarantella CLB fl, ob, cl

WALKER, Richard
  Bagatelle AMP fl, ob, cl
  Capriccio CLB 3 fl
  Cortege CLB 3 fl

WAXMAN, Donald
  Trio for oboe, ob, cl, bsn
    clarinet &
    bassoon GAL

WOODWIND--QUARTETS (fl, ob, cl, bsn unless otherwise indicated)

CACAVAS, John
  Impressions SMC

CHARLTON, Andrew
  Three movements 4 rec
    for 4 recorders
    GAL

DUCKWORTH, William
  Pitch city MEDP any 4 winds
  Reel music MEDP 4 sax

HEUSSENSTAMM, George
  Tetralogue WIM 4 cl & perc
    (See also "Per-
    cussion")

KARLINS, M. William
  Blues TP 4 sax

KATZ, Erich
  Toccata for four 4 rec (SATB)
    recorders AMP

LINN, Robert
  Prelude & dance   4 sax
    WIM
  Quartet (in: 3   4 sax
    contemporary
    saxophone quartets
    WIM

LUNETTA, Stanley
  Free music CPE

McCARTY, Frank
  Five situations for 4 sax
    4 saxophones
    ART

McKAY, George Frederick
  Five pieces WIM   4 cl
  Lyric poem SMC   4 fl

MAURY, Lowndes
  Cock of the walk   4 sax
    (in: 3 contempo-
    rary saxophone
    quartets) WIM

MAXWELL, Charles
  Idyls of four   4 bsn
    goblins WIM

MURPHY, Lyle
  Cadenzas & recita- 4 sax
    tivos from suite,
    "Warm winds"
    WIM
    Notturno. Sirocco.
  Prelude to canon.
  Rondino

MURRAY, Lyn
  Canon à go-go   4 cl
    WIM

OWEN, Harold
  Chamber music   4 cl
    WIM
    Scherzo. Nocturne.
    Fugue
  Four little fugues 4 rec (SATB)
    GAL

SCHMIDT, William
  Suite (in: 3 con-   4 sax
    temporary sax-

ophone quartets)
WIM

STARER, Robert
  Woodwind quartet
    MCA

STONE, Don
  Chorale & fugue 4 rec (SATB)
    GAL

SUMMERS, Stanley
  Allegro breve   4 cl
    WIM

TUTHILL, Burnet
  Quartet SMC   4 sax

WOODWIND--QUINTETS (fl, ob, cl,
bsn, hn, unless otherwise indicated)

AMRAM, David
  Quintet for winds
    CFP

BAMERT, Matthais
  Woodwind quintet GS

BROWN, Rayner
  Three fugues   5 fl
    for 5 flutes
    WIM

CHILDS, Barney
  Fifth wind quintet
    MEDP

EBERHARD, Dennis
  Paraphrases MEDP

HARMON, Robert
  Suite number   5 cl
    one WIM

HOLMES, G. E.
  Castillia: bolero
    CLB

KOHN, Karl
  Little Suite CF

KORN, Peter Jona
  Quintet for winds,
    Op. 40 CFP

KRAFT, Leo
  Partita no. 3 GEN

LINN, Robert
  Woodwind quintet WIM

OLIVER, Harold S.
  Woodwind quintet CF

PERLE, George
  Quintet for winds no. 1
    TP

ROGERS, John E.
  Rotational Arrays
    BCM

RUGOLO, Pete
  Bossa-waltz WIM

RUSSELL, Robert
  Quintet GEN

SCHWARTZ, Elliott
  Interruptions (with tape
    loop) CF
  Telly BCM Composer in-
    structs that instrumentation
    should be of wide register
    balance, from highest to
    lowest and of distinctly dif-
    ferent timbres; also can be
    performed with mixed winds
    & brasses. 4 percussionists,
    3 television sets, 2 radios,
    1 tape

SKOLNIK, Walter
  Pastorale TP

STEIN, Herman
  Sour suite WIM
    Parade. Lullaby. Baga-
    telle. Lucky seven-eight

WASHBURN, Robert
  Quintet for winds OX

WHEAR, Paul
  Quintet for woodwinds
    SMC

WOODWIND--SEXTETS and LARGER

FIELDS, Frank Gaskin
  Chant ritual no. 1 for instr unspec
    12 woodwinds &
    timpani SMPC

GARLICK, Antony
  Piece for 8 clari-   8 cl
    nets SEM

HEIDEN, Bernhard
  Intrada SMC   sax & woodwind
                      quintet

HEUSSENSTAMM, George
  Set for double   2 ob, 2 E-hn,
    reeds WIM   2 bsn

LADERMAN, Ezra
  Octet for winds OX

LESSARD, John
  Octet for winds JC

McBETH, W. Francis
  Canticle SMC   2 fl, 4 hn, 3 trb,
                       bar, tba, glock,
                       vib, mar, chimes
    (See also "Percussion")

MOROSS, Jerome
  Sonatina BB   6 cl

PILLIN, Boris
  Three pieces for   2 ob, 2 E-hn,
    double-reed   2 bsn, c-bsn
    septet WIM

PRESSER, William
  Choral fantasy for
    clarinet choir SMC

TULL, Fisher
  Scherzino   picc, 3 fl, 3 cl,
    B&H   b-cl

WILLIAMS, John T.
Sinfonietta for winds &
  percussion   MCA
(See also "Percussion" and "Band")

WOODWIND--WITH BRASS, VOICE,
KEYBOARD and/or PERCUSSION

ALBERT, Thomas
Sound frames   ob, sax, trb, vib
  MEDP

ALEXANDER, Josef
Festivities   AB   brass ensemble,
                    org or pno

BACH, Jan
Four 2-bit con-   fl, hn
  traptions   MEDP

BEVERSDORF, Thomas
Cathedral music   2 trp, trb, bar,
  KING   org

BROWN, Rayner
Chorale partita   org, 2 trp, 2
  ("Herzliebster   trb
  Jesu")   WIM
Concerto for 2   2 pno, 6 trp, 4
  pianos, brass &   hn, 6 trb, tba,
  percussion   WIM perc, timp

CARTER, Elliott
Canon for 3 (in: for 3 equal in-
  memoriam for   strumental
  Igor Stravinsky) voices
  AMP

CHIHARA, Paul
Willow, willow   fl(amplified b-
  CFP   fl preferred),
                    tba, perc (3
                    players)
(See also "Percussion")

CHILDS, Barney
Music for....   four mov: 2 for
  AMP   unspec instr;
                    one for b-dr;
                    one for ob

COPE, David
Towers   MEDP   unspec instr
                    ensemble

DIAMOND, David
Partita SMPC   ob, bsn, pno

ERB, Donald
Souvenir (a   wind & perc instr
  multi-media   preferred for 12-
  work)   TP   20 players. Length
                    is determined by
                    the electronic tape
                    which is 8 min.
                    Collection of color-
                    ful abstract slides
                    also needed;
                    dancers (opt).
Three pieces for   brass quintet, pno
  brass quintet
  & piano

FELDMAN, Morton
Madam Press   for 13 mixed instr
  died last week at
  ninety   TP

FRACKENPOHL, Arthur
Flute rag EBM   3 fl, pno (rhythm
                    sec. opt)

FULKERSON, James
Now II   MEDP   amplified clavi-
                    chord, oscillators,
                    trp, trb, tape de-
                    lay

GIRON, Arsenio
Sextet for winds   trp, fl, ob, cl,
  & trumpet CF   bsn, hn

HAMM, Charles
Round   MEDP   unspec mixed en-
                    semble

HEINEMAN, John
Views   CPE   3 cl, basset hn (or
                    sax), vib

HENRY, Otto
Omnibus I   unspec mixed en-
  MEDP   semble

HOVHANESS, Alan
Saturn CFP   S, cl, pno (text: A.
                    Hovhaness)
(For contents, see "(Voice) Solo")

KOHN, Karl
Impromptus   fl, cl, 2 bsn, 2 trp,
  CF   2 trb

MACERO, Teo
  Canzona no. 1   4 sax, trp
  NME

McKAY, Francis H.
  The dancer CLB   3 fl, pno

MAXWELL, Charles
  Trio SEM   fl, hn, bsn

MOSS, Lawrence
  Exchanges FER   2 fl, ob, 2 trp,
                        trb, perc

NAGEL, Robert
  Suite for brass &
    piano SF
  March for trombone.
  Adagio for horn.
  Scherzo for tuba. Al-
    legro for trumpet. Finale

NOON, David
  Introduction, dirge   fl/picc, cl, bsn,
    & frolic CF   trp, trb

OWEN, Harold
  Fantasies WIM   3 trp, pno

PHIFER, Larry
  Construction no. 2   3 to 6 instr
    MEDP

PINKHAM, Daniel
  Gloria from "Sin-   2 trp, trb (hn),
    fonia sacra"   bar/trb, org
    KING

READ, Gardner
  Nine by six   fl (picc), ob
    CFP   (E-hn), cl, trp,
                        hn, bsn
  Sinfonia da chiesa   org, brass quin-
    CFP   tet: 2 trp, hn,
                        2 trb
  Intrada. Canzona. Ricercare

REYNOLDS, Roger
  1/0: a ritual for   9 female vocal-
    23 performers   ists, 9 male
    CFP   mimes, cl, 2 fl,
                        2 technician/per-
                        formers who
                        electronically
                        manipulate and
                        distribute the
                        sound.
  (Note: The four sections of 1/0

(A through D) are delineated and
joined by 3 episodes of pre-
verbal expression: anxiety, anger,
mirth)

REYNOLDS, Verne
  Concertare III   woodwind quintet
    CF   & pno

RIEGGER, Wallingford
  Movement PIC   2 trp, trb, pno

RUGOLO, Pete
  Bach & forth   pno, 3 cl
    WIM
  Till we spiegal   pno, 2 hn
    again WIM

SACCO, P. Peter
  Three Psalms   T or S solos,
    WIM   brass quintet
  (For contents, see "(Voice)
  Solo")

SCHMIDT, William
  Vendor's call   pno with cl choir
    WIM   acc

SCHWARTZ, Elliott
  Septet AB   for 5 instr, pno,
                        speaker/singer
  Telly BCM   for 5 winds and/or
                        brass players; 4
                        percussionists,
                        3 television sets,
                        2 radios, 1 tape
  (See also "Woodwind--Quintets")

SIMONS, Netty
  Design groups II   duo for any 2 instr
    TP   of high & low reg-
                        isters

SUBOTNIK, Morton
  Play no. 1 (1964)   pno, wind quintet,
    MCA(R)   tape, film
  Serenade no. 2   cl, hn, pno, perc
    MM(R)

UDOW, Michael
  Understanding   6 unspec instr,
    MEDP   8 parade drum-
                        mers, tape re-
                        corder

WEISLING, Raymond
   Poon Lim ... a   2 fl, cl, bsn,
      night upon the   hn, trb, tba
      waves MEDP

WILDER, Alec
   Suite for French   hn, tba, pno
      horn, tuba & piano
      SF

WOLFF, Christian
   Edges CFP   unspec mixed
                      ensemble

WUORINEN, Charles
   Chamber concerto   solo tba; 4 fl,
      for tuba with 12   2 ob (E-hn), 2
      winds & 12   bsn, 4 hn, perc
      drums CFP(R)   (1 player)

YOUNG, Michael
   Music for organ   org, 2 trp, hn,
      & brass AUG   trb

BRASS--DUOS

DIEMENTE, Edward
Designs SEM   trp, trb

FRACKENPOHL, Arthur
Brass duo KING   hn (bar), tba

HEIDEN, Bernhard
5 canons (1971)   2 hn
AMP

KRAFT, Leo
Dualities GEN   2 trp
Fanfares. March by night.
Polka. Reflection. Galop

LUEDEKE, Raymond
8 bagatelles for   2 tba
2 tubas TP
Wonderland duets   2 tba, Narr
TP   (words by Lewis Carroll)

MAYER, William
Sonata SMC   2 hn

MICHALSKY, Donal
Fantasia a due   b-trb, hn
WIM

PRESSER, William
7 tuba duets TP   2 tba

RAPHLING, Sam
Sonatina EM   2 trb

SACCO, P. Peter
Land of the sky   trp, trb
WIM

UBER, David
10 concert duets   2 trb (unacc)
EM

BRASS--TRIOS

BLOCK, Robert Paul
Incantations &   3 trb
canzona WIM

BUTTS, Carrol
Flamingo trumpets 3 trp with band
CLB   acc

CARTER, Elliott
Canon for 3 (in   for any 3 equal
memoriam for   instr voices
Igor Stravinsky)
AMP

DIEMENTE, Edward
Dimensions I SEM for any 3 instr

DUCKWORTH, William
Transparent in-   trp, hn, trb
terludes CPC

HARMON, Robert
Pascalle WIM   3 trp

HARTLEY, Walter S.
Two pastiches for brass
trio JBI

LEMMON, Douglas
Trio MEDP   2 trp, trb

MAYER, William
County fair TP   2 trp, trb

MUCZYNSKI, Robert
Voyage: Seven   trp, hn, trb
pieces for
trumpet, horn &
trombone GS

PINKHAM, Daniel
Brass trio CFP   trp, hn, trb

RAPHLING, Sam
3 pieces for brass   trp, hn, trb
trio GEN

SCHMIDT, William
Chamber music for   trp, hn, trb
three brass WIM

98

SKOLNIK, Walter
    Little suite in F TP   3 trb

SNYDER, Randall
    Dance suite   trp, hn, trb
      WIM

TANNER, Paul
    Imitation WIM   3 trb
    Larghetto WIM   3 trb

UBER, David
    Contemporary trios 3 trb
      Op. 54 CFP
      Midsummer reverie. Dancing
      elves. Track meet. Autumn
      mood. Vermont pastures
    Five concert trios, 3 trb
      Op. 53 CFP
      Reflection. Choreographer's de-
      light. Gettysburg elegy. Taran-
      tella. Dance of the slides
    Manhattan vignettes   3 trb
      EM
    Three chorales,   3 trb
      Op. 55 CFP

WINICK, Steven
    Confrontation for   trp, hn, trb
      brass trio JBI

BRASS--QUARTETS

BAVICCHI, John
    Quartet no. 1 for   2 trp, 2 trb
      brass, Op. 22 OX

BEVERSDORF, Thomas
    Three epitaphs   2 trp, hn, trb
      SMC

BOTTJE, Will Gay
    Chorale & allegro   4 trp
      CPC

HYDE, George
    Suite for 4 trom-   4 trb
      bones WIM

IAMMACCONE, Anthony
    Three mythical   2 bar-hn, 2 tba
      sketches TP
      Pluto. Persephone. Poseidon

JACOB, Gordon
    Scherzo GAL   2 trp, hn, trb

McKAY, Francis H.
    Interlude CLB   cor, hn, 2 trb
    Suite for 4 horns   4 hn
      CLB
      Canzonetta. Chorale. Boat song.
      Nocturne. Allegro moderato

PIKET, Frederick
    Dance & March   2 trp, 2 trb
      AMP

PRESSER, William
    Chaconne &   4 trb
      March TP
    Serenade TP   4 tba
    Suite for brass
      quartet CF

RUGOLO, Pete
    Four trump   4 trp
      WIM
    Razing the 7th   2 trp, 2 trb
      WIM

SNYDER, Randall
    Ricercar KING   2 hn, 2 trb

STARER, Robert
    Dirge TP   2 trp, 2 trb

TANNER, Paul
    Just Bach WIM 4 trb

VAN de VATE, Nancy
    Short suite for   2 trp, 2 trb
      brass quartet
      TP

BRASS--QUINTETS (2 trp, hn, trb, tba unless otherwise indicated)

CAMPO, Frank
    Madrigals and who shall guard the
      guardians? WIM
      1. Indifference
      2. Unrequited love
      3. Aria perduta

CHEETHAM, John
    Scherzo WIM

DAHL, Ingolf
  Music for brass   2 trp, hn, 2 trb
    instruments WIM (or trb, tba)

ELLIS, Merrill
  Mutations--a multi-
    media composition
    with electronic tape,
    dancers, 16 mm film,
    & 35 mm slides SHAW

ERICKSON, Robert
  Ricercare a 5   with tape, 5
    SEM   trb (also for
        solo trb)

FRACKENPOHL, Arthur
  Brass quintet no. 2
    KING

FREDERICKSON, Thomas
  Brass quintet CPC

GIRON, Arsenio
  Disparities & differ-
    ences CF

HADDAD, Don
  Jazz etude SMC

HAINES, Edmund
  Sonata for brass quintet
    KING

KAPLAN, Nathan Ivan
  Fugue on fugue CHAP

KUPFERMAN, Meyer
  Brass quintet (1970) 2 trp, hn, 2 trb
    GEN   (or trb, tba)

LEE, William F.
  Mosaics CHH

McKAY, George Frederick
  Sonatina expressiva SMC

MOROSS, Jerome
  Sonatina for brass
    quintet CHAP

MORYL, Richard
  Soundings GEN

POLIN, Claire
  Cader Idris (Landscape
    for brass quintet) GS

PRESSER, William
  Folk song fantasy SEM

REYNOLDS, Verne
  Centone no. 1 through
    no. 8 SMC
    (published separately)
  Concertare I CF with perc
  Suite for brass
    quintet MCA
    Toccata. Chorale. Scherzo.
    Arioso. March

ROSS, Walter
  Concerto for brass quintet
    & orchestra B&H(R)
    I. Introduction & toccata
    II. Intermezzo notturno
    III. Variations

SCHMIDT, William
  Suite no. 3 WIM
    Praeludium. Quasi recitativo.
    Fantasia. Scherzando. Chorale

SCHWARTZ, Elliott
  Telly BCM
    composer instructs that
    instrumentation should
    be of wide register bal-
    ance, from highest to
    lowest and of distinctly
    different timbres. Can
    also be performed by 5
    woodwinds or by mixed
    winds & brasses. 4 per-
    cussionists, 3 television
    sets, 2 radios, 1 tape

SHINN, Randall
  Serenade for brass
    quintet KING

STEIN, Alan
  Quintessence   5 trb
    MEDP

SVOBODA, Tomas
  Chorale & dance 2 trp, 2 trb, tba
    COL

UBER, David
  Streets of Laredo, Op. 60:
    theme & variations for
    brass quintet CF

WASHBURN, Robert
  Quintet for brass OX

WHITTENBERG, Charles
Triptych GEN
I. Rotational games: scherzo
II. Sostenuto (in memory of
Anton Webern)
III. Canonic fanfares

BRASS--SEXTETS and LARGER

ADLER, Samuel
Brass fragments   large ensemble
SMC

BERNSTEIN, Leonard
Shivaree (fanfare   large ensemble
for double brass
ensemble & percus-
sion) GS
(See also "Percussion")

BEVERSDORF, Thomas
Cathedral music   brass choir
SMC

BLATTER, Alfred W.
Suite for 10   4 trp, 2 hn, 2
brasses CPC   trb, bar, tba

BROWN, Rayner
Fantasy-fugue   4 trp, 4 hn, 4
WIM   trb, tba, timp,
(See also "Per-   perc
cussion")

CAMPO, Frank
Suite for brass   2 trp, 2 hn, 2
WIM   trb, tba

COLLECTION OF FANFARES (1969)
FOR 8 TRUMPETS WIM   8 trp
Note: Composers in this collec-
tion include: Irving Bush, Jef-
frey Reynolds, Frank Campo,
Fred Dutton, William Kraft,
William Schmidt & Leonard Rosen-
man

De JONG, Conrad
Three studies for   3 trp, 3 trb, tba
brass septet WIM

GOULD, Morton
Columbian fan-   brass septet
fares BB

KUPFERMAN, Meyer
Concertino for 11   4 trp, 2 hn, 4
brass instru-   trb, tba
ments GEN

LUENING, Otto
Fanfare for a   3 trp, 3 hn, 3 trb,
festive occa-   bells, cmb, timp
sion CFP

McKAY, Francis H.
Seven pieces for   (2 trp, hn, trb,
brass sextets CLB bar, tba)
Concert prelude   2 cor, hn, trb,
bar, tba)
Dramatic prelude
Fantasy
Grandioso
Narrative sketch
Second fantasy
Sextet in A-major
(Note: Above sextets available
only separately)

MAILMAN, Martin
Two fanfares   large ensemble
SMC

PISTON, Walter
Ceremonial fanfare 4 trp, 6 hn, 3
AMP   trb, tba, timp,
perc
(See also "Percussion")

RILEY, James
Suite for brass   3 trp, 4 hn, bar,
choir TP   3 trb, tba
Dance Americana. Interlude. Fan-
fare/chorale (fugue)

SACCO, P. Peter
Study for brass &   3 trp, 2 trb,
percussion WIM   bar, tba, perc
(See also "Percussion")

SHULMAN, Alan
Two chorales for   large ensemble
brass SHAW

STABILE, James
Suite for brass   6 trp, 6 trb, tba,
choir WIM   timp

STOUT, Alan
Pieta JBI   large ensemble
(See also "(Orchestra) String")

SYDEMAN, William
  Music for brass   large ensemble
    ensemble & per-   & perc
    cussion OKM
  (See also "Percussion")

THOMSON, Virgil
  Metropolitan Mu-   large ensemble
    seum fanfare GS

WEINER, Lawrence
  Suite for brass sextet
    SMC

WUENSCH, Gerhard
  Music for seven   3 trp, 3 trb,
    brass WIM   tba

ZANINELLI, Luigi
  Music for a solemn   5 trp, 3 trb, b-
    occasion TP   trb, tba, timp,
                         2 sn-dr, cmb,
                         large gong
  (Note: If performed by large brass
  choir, all parts except percussion
  may be doubled.)

4. CONCERT JAZZ

(Jazz combos and big band jazz)

LEVITT, Rod
2d stage band se-
ries AMP   2 a-sax, 2 t-
sax, bar-sax, 4
trp, 4 trb, gtr,
c-b, pno, dr
1. Cathedral city
2. Circle five
3. M'lord is at Olympia house
4. Onion chicken
5. Woodman of the world
(for 1st stage band series, see
Concert Music by American Composers, 2nd edition (1969), p.251)

LIEB, Dick
Bossa fair FM

MADDEN, Edward J.
Rock movement for
band EBM
(See also "Band")

RICHARDS, Johnny
Bochica ("Chia
transformed")
AMP   5 sax, 4 trp, 4
trb, c-b, gtr,
pno, dr, bongos,
tam
Don Camillo AMP   same instr as
above
Macaw AMP   same instr as
above

SEIBERT, Bob
Jazz suite KSM   8 brass, 5 sax
Theme & varia-   8 brass, 5 sax
tions in jazz KSM

SERIES OF PUBLICATIONS FOR STAGE
& JAZZ BANDS CLB   4/5 trp, 4/5
trb, 5 sax, tba
(b-trb), gtr, c-
b, dr, perc, pno
(this instrumen-
tation varies

slightly for some
of the works listed)
I. Mod-rock: play-easy series for
stage band
Russ Martino: Cast a spell. Solid
soul. Soul brother.
Torrey pines
II. New dimensions for jazz band
Paul Clark: Something for Shelly
Jack Cortner: Santa Anna
Robert Lowden: Goldfrost
Joe South: Games people play

III. New dimensions for stage band
Dick Fenno: Another shade of
blue. The golden
horns. Everybody's
rockin'. Purple
mist. Santana wind.
Strollin'. Take
three. Mr. Tubbs.
Uptown groove
Robert Lowden: B.J.'s thing.
Dominova. 5=4=3.
Five for five.
Nancy's dream
Russ Martino: Lament for joy
Ralph Mutchler: Wiggy
Hale Rood: Finchwalk

IV. Play-easy series for stage band
Russ Martino: Coo's blues. Eau
de groove. Sassy
lassy. Soul sister.
Sugar plum. Sweet
'n' steady. The
waddle
(Note: All works listed above are
available only separately)

5. PERCUSSION[*]

BAIRD, James
A stroll on the bottom of the sea
  for 3 percussionists MEDP

BAVICCHI, John
Music for mallets & percussion   glock, xy, mar, vib, drm, cmb, wood-
  OX   blocks, tam, tri, timp
Trio no. 3 SEM   pno, 2 perc

BECK, John Ness
Concepts for timpani BOS   timp
Jazz variants BOS   perc ensemble of 8 players: I. vibes;
                                         II. mar; III. bells & tam; IV. chimes,
                                         bell three, quiro, tri, bongos; V. susp
                                         cmb, cowbell, b-dr, tam, congo dr;
                                         VI. bell three, tam, bongos, 4 tom-
                                         toms; VII. 4 timp; VIII. dr set

Rhapsody for percussion & band
  BOS
Sonata for timpani BOS   4 dr

BELLSON, Louis
Percussion suite no. 1 for 5   1. chochalo shaker, sn-dr, xy;
  players WIM   2. sn-dr, tam, xy; 3. claves,
                                         cowbell, pic, sn-dr, tam, xy; 4. dr
                                         set; 5. timp

BERNSTEIN, Leonard
Shivaree (fanfare for double brass
  & percussion) GS

BROWN, Rayner
Fantasy-fugue WIM   4 trp, 4 hn, 4 trb, tba, timp, perc

BRUCE, Neely
Three canons for marimba MEDP   mar

BUDD, Harold
Obos CPE   cmb (chimes), cel, Haiku reader

---

[*]For some works, instrumentation was unspecified; for others, it was not
available.

BUTTS, Carrol
  Percussion for five CLB   2 sn-dr, t-dr, b-dr, timp (5 players)

CHIHARA, Paul
  Branches CFP   2 bsn, 8 dr, gong, temple block
  Logs CFP   multiple basses, wind chimes, pre-
                                    recorded tape
  Willow, willow CFP   fl, tba, perc: 3 timp, b-dr, gong, 4
                                    roto toms, susp cmb, b-dr, gong,
                                    tri, tubular chimes

CHILDS, Barney
  Jack's new bag CPE   fl, trp, trb, pno (2 players), perc I:
                                    2 timp, 3 tom-toms, 2 temple blocks,
                                    gong, susp cmb, sn-dr, tri; perc II:
                                    jazz dr set, vla, vlc, c-b

COLGRASS, Michael
  Rhapsodic fantasy MCA(R)   3 perc soloists with cham orch
  Two unaccompanied solos for   sn-dr
    snare drum GS

COPE, David
  Obelisk for 5 percussionists
    MEDP

CRESTON, Paul
  Ceremonial GS   perc ensemble & pno
  Meditation GS   mar & org

CROLEY, Randell
  Concerto for flute & metal or-
    chestra JBI
  Partita for percussion (1 player)
    JBI

CUNNINGHAM, Michael
  Polyphonies for percussion quartet
    MEDP

DAVIS, Thomas L.
  Bossa novacaine CLB   mallet I & II, claves, bongos, timp,
                                    susp cmb (6 players)
  Three-for-all CLB   susp cmb, sn-dr, tri, woodblock,
                                    orch bells, timp (6 players)

De GASTYNE, Serge
  Alborada FER   vibraharp
  Lyrique FER   mar
  Menuet tres antique FER   vibraharp

DUCKWORTH, William
  Gambit MEDP   solo perc & tape
  Time fields MEDP   solo perc

EBERHARD, Dennis
  Chamber music MEDP   2 percussionists

EHLE, Robert C.
  Algorhythms   CF
  Pieces for instruments with pre-
    pared electronics   CF

S, prepared pno, cl, c-b
1. Hypersonde--prepared pno
2. Mordorisund--prepared vln
3. Sundridod--prepared cl
4. Rock music--prepared perc
5. Estrangeon--prepared pno, vln, cl, perc

ERB, Donald
  Diversion for two for trumpet &
    percussion   TP

trp; glock, sn-dr, vib, blocks, timbales, cmb, chimes, xy, b-dr, 5
timp, slide whistle

  Four for percussion   MP

8 players: 1. cel; 2. hp; 3. pno; 4.
xy, glock, chimes, vibes; 5. sn-dr,
susp cmb, claves, tam; 6. 2 tri,
finger cmb, tenor, susp cmb, whip,
temple blocks; 7. cmb, bongos, wood
blocks, b-dr, maracas, large gong,
ratchet, cmb; 8. 4 timp

  Kyrie   TP

SATB divisi, pno, electric tape; perc:
4 susp cmb, 4 woodblocks, 2 sn-dr,
b-dr, timp, xy, vib;
perc to be played by the choir: S:
large claves; A: small claves; T:
bongos; B: maracas   text: liturgical

ETLER, Alvin
  XL plus one for multiple percus-
    sion solo   SMC

41 perc instr to be played by one percussionist: metal, wood & membrane
instr are grouped in a suggested set-
up in score

FELDSTEIN, Saul
  Multiple percussion music   AMC

score includes 18 solos for a number
of instr, ranging from 1 to 5

FINNEY, Ross Lee
  2 acts for 3 players   CFP

cl, pno, perc

FLAGELLO, Nicolas
  Electra   MP

pno solo, cel, hp, perc (7 players):
1. mar, finger cmb, xy, glock, b-dr,
   chimes, sn-dr, vibes, gong, tri,
   b-mar;
2. glock, sn-dr, susp cmb, b-dr, vibes,
   chimes, mar, tri, 3 tom-toms,
   finger cmb;
3. b-dr, susp cmb, gong, temple
   blocks, glock, woodblock, tam, tri,
   finger cmb, flexatone, sn-dr

FRACKENPOHL, Arthur
  Introduction & romp   GS

mar or vib (or fl) solo, pno

FRAZEUR, Theodore
  Mood piece   MP

vibes, 2 timbales, 2 timp

FROCK, George
   Three Asiatic dances   SMC

6 players using conventional perc instr
& a part for 5 metal sounds such as
brake dr or metal pipes

FULKERSON, James
   Mobiles & loops   MEDP

4 perc & tape

GILBERT, Donald K.
   Soliloquy for percussion   SMC

5 players using concert tom-toms,
timp, mar, sn-dr, cmb, chimes, b-dr

GIRON, Arsenio
   Vias   CF

fl, cl, vlc, pno, perc: glock, xy,
vib, 2 t-dr, 2 susp cmb, 5 temple
blocks

GOTTLIEB, Jay
   Synchronisms   SEM

2 perc & tape

GRIEVE, Annette
   Chamber music   MEDP

2 perc

HENEY, John J.
   Dawn patrol   CLB

sn-dr trio

HENRY, Otto
   Do not pass go   MEDP
   Liberty bell   MEDP
   Omnibus I & II   MEDP
   Sons of Martha   MEDP

3 timp (2 players)
10 perc & tape
unspec nonpitched & pitched perc
S, 4 perc

HERDER, Ronald
   Requiem II,   games of power
     AMP(R)
   (See also "(Voice) Solo" and
   "Chorus--Men's"; "String--
   with Voice, Winds and/or
   Percussion")

m-S solo with men's ch, 2 trp, 2 hn,
3 trb, pno/cel, 2 c-b, electronic tape,
perc: vib, timp, antique cmb, tri,
susp cmb, medium dr, deep dr, b-dr
text: Giacomo Leopardi; trans: John
Heath-Stubbs & Iris Origo
(See also "Voice Solo" and "Chorus--
Men's; String--with Voice, Winds
and/or Perc.")

HEUSSENSTAMM, George
   Tetralogue   WIM

4 cl; perc (1 player): vib, cmb, dr,
tri, gong, tom-tom

HILLER, Lejaren & R. Baker
   Computer cantata   NME

S, instr ensemble (unspec), 2-channel
tape recorder

KEAGLE, Roger
   Three movements for percussion
     ensemble   MP

6 players: 4 small dr, 4 med-dr, 4
large dr, sn-dr, large b-dr, 4 timp,
bells, xy, maracas, chimes, mar,
temple blocks, cmb, castanets,
claves, 2 woodblocks

KOHN, Karl
   Rhapsodies   CF

mar, vib, perc (1 player)

KRAFT, William
  Encounters III WIM   perc (1 player) & trp
    Strategy. Truce of God. Tactics
  Momentum for percussion SMC   unspec perc ensemble

LAZAROF, Henri
  Asymptotes AMP   fl, vib
  Cadence III AMP   vln, perc (2 players)

McBETH, W. Francis
  Canticle SMC   2 fl, 4 hn, 3 trb, bar, tba, glock,
                      vib, mar, chimes

MacBRIDE, David
  Envelop MEDP   solo perc

McCARTY, Frank
  Clocks MEDP   for 5 percussionists

McKENZIE, Jack
  Paths I & II MEDP   solo perc
    (for sale only separately)
  Suite for sideman & handclappers
    (2 players) MEDP

MEISTER, Scott R.
  Pagan place LMP   4 players using xy, bongos, timp,
                      chimes, tam-tam, b-dr, tri

MORGAN, Robert
  Piece of eight MEDP   2 players

MOSS, Lawrence
  Timepiece for violin, piano &   perc: 4 timp, 3 t-dr, vib, 3 susp
    percussion FER   cmb, tam-tam, chimes

NOON, David
  Inflections CF   pno, prepared pno, hpcd, hp, vib
  Sonata CF   cl, vib, prepared pno

O'CONNER, G. Allan
  Multi-percussion solos nos. 2 & 1 player
    3 MEDP
  Rondo MEDP   1 player

ODONNELL, Rich
  Microtimbre I MEDP   amplified tam-tam

OLIVEROS, Pauline
  Trio MEDP   fl, c-b, perc

O'REILLY, John
  Three episodes for percussion 5 players: sn-dr, field dr, wood-
    ensemble GS   block, guiro, susp cmb, 4 tom-
                      toms, b-dr

PARCHMAN, Gen
  Concerto for 1 percussionist &
    orchestra SEM(R)

Concerto for percussion ensemble
  & orchestra SEM(R)
2nd concerto for percussion en-   6 perc & timp
  semble & orchestra SEM(R)
3rd symphony for percussion en-   4 perc
  semble SEM(R)
4th symphony for percussion en-   4 perc
  semble SEM(R)
5th symphony for percussion en-   6 perc, pno, c-b, timp
  semble SEM(R)
Sonata for viola & percussion SEM
Symphony for brass & percussion
  SEM(R) (instr for above unspec)

PETERS, Mitchell
  Chant for marimba KSM   mar
  March of the eagles KSM   2 timp, sn-dr, 2 tom-toms, cmb,
                                       b-dr
  Perpetual motion KSM   sn-dr, 4 tom-toms
  Piece for percussion   KSM   sn-dr, xy, 3 tom-toms, bells, casta-
                                       nets, 3 timp, 3 temple blocks, b-dr,
                                       tam, tri, susp cmb, chimes
  Rondino KSM   solo for 4 timp

PHILLIPS, Peter
  Music for percussion AMP   7 players (instr NA)

PILLIN, Boris
  Duo for percussion & piano WIM   pno; perc: xy, vib, sn-dr, t-dr, b-
                                       dr, bongos, susp cmb, cow bell,
                                       temple blocks

PISTON, Walter
  Ceremonial fanfare AMP   6 hn, 4 trp, 3 trb, tba, perc (2
                                       players): timp, tam, sn-dr, tam-tam,
                                       b-dr

RAAB, Emil
  March for percussion MP   6 players: 1. sn-dr; 2. timp; 3. tri;
                                       4. cmb; 5. b-dr, gong; 6. tam

REMSEN, Eric
  The downfall of the rudimentalist   sn-dr solo
    WIM

REYNOLDS, Verne
  Concertare I for brass quintet
    & percussion CF

ROBERTS, Myron J.
  Five for marimba & organ   mar, org
    HWG

ROGERS, Bernard
  Mirage for marimba SMPC   mar

ROSS, Walter
  Five dream sequences for piano &   pno; perc I: bells, cmb, tom-tom;
    percussion quartet B&H (R)   perc II: vib, woodblocks, guiro, ma-
                                         racas, 5 temple blocks, large tam-
                                         tam, timbales; perc III: mar, susp
                                         cmb, 2 tom-toms, ratchet, claves;
                                         perc IV: xy, chimes, castanets, b-dr

SACCO, P. Peter
  Study for brass & percussion   3 trp, 2 trb, bar, tba, timp, susp
    WIM   cmb, sn-dr, t-dr

SARRACCO, John
  Timpian fantasy AB   timp, pno

SCHINSTINE, William J.
  Centralization SMC   5 players: 1. sn-dr, susp cmb; 2.
                                         field dr, tri; 3. crash cmb, casta-
                                         nets; 4. b-dr, tam; 5. timbale, bells
                                         or mar

  Quartet for percussion SMC
  Scherzo for percussion SMC

SCHMIDT, William
  Ludus Americanus WIM   Narr (poems, "Gunslinger" & "House
                                         wife" by William Pillin), perc acc
  The percussive rondo WIM   perc quartet
  Spirituals for cello & percussion
    WIM

SCHWARTZ, Elliott
  Telly BCM   5 winds and/or brasses--composer in-
                                         structs that these instr be of wide reg-
                                         ister balance and of distinctly differ-
                                         ent timbres; 3 television sets; 2 radios,
                                         1 tape, 4 percussionists, as follows:
                                         I: xy (or mar), maracas, 3 bells;
                                         II: susp cmb, 2 woodblocks, tri &
                                         beater, tam; III: 2 timp, 1 small
                                         transistor radio; IV: 3 dr (bongos,
                                         tom-toms, etc.) of graduated sizes;
                                         1 small b-dr with strap attachment for
                                         marching; 1 small transistor radio

SHRADER, David
  Variations on an Indian tala   2 unspec perc
    MEDP

SIFLER, Paul
  Marimba suite WIM   mar
    Prelude--ostinato. Scherzetto.
    Carillon. Toccata

SIMONS, Netty
  Design groups I TP   1-3 players. Choice of instr left to
                                         performer(s)
  Silver thaw TP   1-8 players. Choice of instr left to
                                         performer(s)

SIWE, Thomas
    Sextet MP

6 players: 1. claves; 2. bongo dr;
3. maracas; 4. timbales; 5. woodblock; 6. timp

SMITH, Stuart
    A fine old tradition MEDP
    One for syl MEDP
    Poems I, II, III MEDP

sax, electric pno, pno, perc
vib
Narr (text: S. Smith), 5 brake dr

SPEARS, Jared
    Prologue & jubilo for multiple
      percussion solo SMC

1st mov: 2 timp & bells
2nd mov.: susp cmb, 4 tom-toms, 2
timp

STABILE, James
    Ballade (Night song) WIM

vib

STEG, Paul
    Targets MEDP

perc solo with lighting

SYDEMAN, William
    Duo for 2 percussionists OKM
    Music for brass ensemble & per-
      cussion OKM
    Music for viola, winds & percus-
      sion OKM

TOWER, Joan
    Percussion quartet MP

4 players: 1. sm-dr, cowbell, woodblock, anvil pipe; 2. large tri, 2 tam;
3. med-cmb, timp; 4. large gong,
b-dr

TULL, Fisher
    Sonatina for percussion ensemble
      B&H

perc I: wood blocks, tri, sn-dr, tam-
tam, antique cmb; perc II: tam, cmb,
susp cmb, slapstick, xy, vib; perc III:
temple blocks, t-dr, timbales, glock;
perc IV: timp, bongo dr

UDOW, Michael
    Understanding MEDP

6 unspec instr, 8 parade drummers,
tape recorder

WAGNER, Joseph
    A festive fanfare for brass & per-
      cussion SF

WEINBERG, Henry
    Cantus commemorabilis I
      MCA(R)

cham orch, perc I: 2 pedal timp,
3 susp cmb, xy, 3 Chinese blocks,
guiro; perc II: pno, 2 sn-dr, chalco,
maracas

WEISLING, Raymond
    Essence of ampersand MEDP

cl & perc

WHALEY, Gar
  Danza al Greco   RAL   5 players: 2 timp, sn-dr, b-dr, 3
                                          tom-toms, cmb
  Dialogue for snare drum & per-   sn-dr, perc
    cussion RAL
  Interplay for percussion sextet   6 players: xy, bells, 2 timp, sn-dr,
    RAL   b-dr, cmb
  Scherzo for timpani RAL   4 timp

WILLIAMS, John T.
  Sinfonietta for winds & percus-   minimum of 6 players: timp, sn-dr,
    sion MCA(R)   3 pitched dr, b-dr, tri, 2 susp tri,
                                          med large gong, mar, vib, xy, cmb,
                                          2 susp cmb, chimes, bells, high
                                          pitched metal bar

  (See also "Band")

WUORINEN, Charles
  Janissary music CFP   1 player
  Ringing changes CFP   2 vib, pno (4 hands), 12 graduated dr
                                          (2 players), 6 anvils (or brake dr &
                                          6 almglocken) (2 players), 6 cmb, 4
                                          tam-tams

WYTON, Alec
  Concert piece for organ & percus-
    sion JF

ZONN, Paul
  Xoe MEDP   solo perc

6. ORCHESTRA

STRING--ORCHESTRA

	Duration* (min)
CHESCOE, E. Conversation piece AMP	5
DELLO JOIO, Norman Choreography EBM	9
HOVHANESS, Alan Armenian rhapsody no. 3 CFP	6
MAYER, William Andante for strings MCA(R)	3

RACKLEY, Lawrence
    Variations on a theme of
    Handel CAP
	7

ROREM, Ned Pilgrims B&H(R)	6
RUDHYAR, Dane Five stanzas NME	

	Duration* (min)
SHULMAN, Alan Threnody TP	5.5

STOUT, Alan
    Pieta JBI
    (See also "(Instr Ensemble)
    Brass--Sextets and larger")	

WASHBURN, Robert Serenade for strings OX	8

WEINER, Lawrence
    Quaternity: suite in 4
    movements   LMP
	5

WHEAR, Paul W. Preludio LMP	4

ORCHESTRA--SMALL or CHAMBER†

		Duration* (min)
CAGAN, Steven Suite for the dance SMPC		

COPLAND, Aaron
  Suite from "Appalachian Spring"
    for 13 instruments (original
    scoring) B&H
	fl, cl, bsn, pno, 4 vln,
	2 vla, 2 vlc, c-b
		25

DRUCKMAN, Jacob Incenters for 13 instruments MCA	fl, cl, bsn, hn, trp, trb, org, pno, vln, vla, vlc, c- b, perc	12

*Approximate. In some instances, no timing indicated in the score.
† Instrumentation given when indicated in the score or from information
from the publisher.

Duration*
(min)

FOSTER, Stephen (H. Wiley Hitchcock, Ed.)
  The social orchestra DCP
  (A little-known collection of ar-
    rangements by Foster himself of
    many of his songs. It includes
    also the sets of quadrilles, "Vil-
    lage festival" and "Old folks.")

HEINRICH, Anthony Philip (1781-1861)
(H. Wiley Hitchcock, Ed.)
  The dawning of music in Kentucky
    (or the pleasures of harmony in
    the solitudes of nature)--opera
    prima DCP
  The Western minstrel--opera sec-
    onda DCP
  (Note: Both above are collections by
    America's first romantic nationalist
    and contain songs, waltzes, cotillions,
    minuets, polonaises, marches, etc.)

HEISS, John
  Four short pieces MEDP   2 fl, 2 ob, 2 cl, 2 bsn,   6
                                       2 hn, str

HOVHANESS, Alan
  Mountains & rivers without end,   7
    Op. 225 CFP

IVES, Charles
  The circus band for mixed chorus   3
    (optional) & small orchestra PIC

KAY, Ulysses
  Scherzi musicali for chamber   fl, ob, cl, hn, bsn, vln (I   17
    orchestra MCA(R)   & II), vla, vlc, c-b

LAZAROF, Henri
  Espaces AMP(R)   2 fl, 2 cl, 2 vla, 2 vlc,   15.5
    Acte I.   Entr'acte I.   2 pno
    Acte II.   Entr'acte II.
    Acte III

PINKHAM, Daniel (arr.)
  Music for a merry Christmas CFP (Instr varies)   varies
    Adeste fidelis. Angel voices.
    All my heart this night rejoices.
    The birds. Coventry carol. Deck
    the halls. The first nowell. God
    rest you merry gentlemen. Good
    King Wencelas. Greensleeves. The
    holly and the ivy. In dulce jubilo.
    Joy to the world. March of the
    kings. Silent night. Sing we now.
    O tannenbaum. Wassail. We
    three kings.
    (Note: all above titles available only separately.)

		Duration* (min)
SCHWARTZ, Elliott		
Texture AB(R)	fl, ob, cl, bsn, hn, trp, trb, 2 vln, vla, vlc, c-b	7
WAGNER, Joseph		
Pastoral costarricense ("Costa Rican pastoral") MCA(R)	fl, ob, cl, bsn, 2 hn, cel, vln (I & II), vla, c-b, timp, perc (chimes, tam, bells)	10
WEINBERG, Henry		
Cantus commemorabilis 1 MCA(R)	fl(dbl picc), ob(dbl E-hn), cl(dbl b-cl), hn, trp, b-trb, perc I & II, pno, vln, vlc, c-b	8
YARDUMIAN, Richard		
Armenian suite EV(R) (See also "Full Symphony")		16

ORCHESTRA--STRING or CHAMBER with SOLO INSTRUMENT or VOICE

	Solo	Duration (min)
BROWN, Rayner		
Concerto WIM	org; str	
COLGRASS, Michael		
Rhapsodic fantasy MCA(R)	perc(3 soloists); cham	8
HOVHANESS, Alan		
Sosi (forest of prophetic sounds) PIC	vln; str & hn, timp, giant tam-tam, pno	10
LAZAROF, Henri		
Textures AMP(R)	pno; cham	23.5
PARCHMAN, Gen		
3rd symphony for percussion & strings SEM(R)	perc; str	26
PRESSER, William		
Concerto TP(R)	tba; str	10
ROREM, Ned		
Water music B&H(R)	cl & vln; cham	17
SACCO, P. Peter		
Daybreak WIM	med voice; str (text: Henry W. Longfellow)	2
Deceive me once again WIM	med voice; str (text: Walter Savage Landor)	3

	Solo	Duration* (min)
That silent land WIM	med voice; str (text: Edward Hoy)	3

(Note: the above songs are also included in
Collected songs, Vol. 1; for contents see "(Voice) Solo")

STEVENS, Halsey
Concerto   PIC   cl; str   20

WEINBERG, Henry
Cantus commemorabilis   MCA(R)   perc; cham   8
(for instr, see "Percussion")

WILLIS, Richard
Recitative & dance   TP(R)   fl; str   5

YARDUMIAN, Richard
Work for flute & strings (untitled)   fl; str   6
EV(R)

ORCHESTRA--FULL SYMPHONY (for classical orchestra (winds in pairs)
or larger)

	Duration (min)		Duration (min)
ARGENTO, Dominick		COPLAND, Aaron	
A ring of time: preludes	28	Three Latin American	
& pageants for orchestra		sketches B&H(R)	
& bells B&H(R)		Danza de Jalisco.	
Spring. Summer. Fall.		Paisage Mexicano.	
Winter. Postlude: homage		Estribillo	
to Gustav Mahler			
		CRUMB, George	
BARBER, Samuel		Echoes of time & the	varies
Fadograph of a yestern		river: four procession-	
scene GS(R)		als for orchestra BEL/	
Under the willow tree (country		MIL(R)	
dance from Vanessa) GS(R)		I. Frozen time	
		II. Remembrance of time	
BASSETT, Leslie		III. Collapse of time	
Colloquy CFP(R)	10	IV. Last echoes of time	
BERGSMA, William		DANIELS, M. L.	
Dances from a New England	8	Festique LMP	6
album, "1856" GAL			
March with trumpets GAL	6	De GASTYNE, Serge	
		Symphony no. 5 FER(R)	30
BERKOWITZ, Sol			
Diversion FM	2.5	DIEMER, Emma Lou	
		Rondo concertante B&H	4.5
BROWN, Earle			
Modules 1 & 2 TP	varies but, acc to com- poser, not fewer than 10 min.	EPSTEIN, David Sonority-variations MCA(R)	20

Orchestra: Full Symphony

	Duration (min)

ERB, Donald
The seventh trumpet TP(R)
Symphony of overtures:
impressions of four mod-
ern plays GAL(R)

FELDMAN, Morton
In search of an orchestra-
tion TP
Of sound & the instrumental
factor TP

FINNEY, Ross Lee
Symphony concertante CFP(R) 40

FULEIHAN, Anis
Symphony no. 2 B&H(R) 25
Three Cyprus serenades 13
SMPC(R)

GUTCHE, Gene
Epimetheus USA, Op. 46 8
GAL(R)
Symphony no. 6, Op. 45 28
GAL(R)

HANSON, Howard
Symphony no. 6 CF(R) 20

HEIDEN, Bernhard
Partita AMP(R)

HOVHANESS, Alan
Ode to the temple of sound 14
CFP(R)
Symphony no. 12 CFP(R) 25
(with mixed chorus: SATB)
I. Andante
II. The Lord is my shepherd
(Psalm 23)
III. Bird of dawn
IV. He leadeth me (Psalm 23)
Symphony no. 22: CFP(R) 21
"City of light"

IMBRIE, Andrew
Symphony no. 1 SHAW(R)

IVES, Charles
Symphony no. 1 PIC(R) 37

JONES, Charles
Hymn CFP(R) 5

KAY, Hersey
The clowns (a ballet) B&H(R) 25

KAY, Ulysses
Theater set MCA(R) 15
1. Overture
2. Ballad; Chase music
3. Finale

KIRCHNER, Leon
Music for orchestra 13
AMP(R)

KLAUSS, Noah
Fantasy for orchestra S-B 11

KRAFT, William
Contextures: riots-- 25
decade '60 MCA(R)

KURKA, Robert
Symphony no. 2, Op. 24 25
WEIN(R)

MARTINO, Donald
Mosaic for grand orchestra 15
ECS(R)

MAYER, William
Two pastels MCA(R) 13

MOROSS, Jerome
Beguine NME 4
Paeans NME 5

PERLE, George
Six bagatelles for orchestra 5.5
TP(R)
(Note: nos. 1, 3 & 6 are published
in a piano solo version (as pre-
ludes) in the album, New music
for piano, published by Lawson-
Gould Music Publishers, Inc.)

PHILLIPS, Peter
Novasonic AMP(R) 14.5

READ, Gardner
Pennsylvaniana suite, Op. 16
67 COL(R)
1. Dunlap's creek
2. I'm a beggar
3. John Riley
Symphony no. 3, Op. 75 25
COL(R)

ROGERS, Bernard
Variations on a song by Mus- 24
sorgsky (a child's song, 1868)
TP(R)

	Duration (min)
RUDHYAR, Dane	
Sinfonietta NME(R)	
RUGGLES, Carl	
Men & mountains AME(R)	20
SCHULLER, Gunther	
Composition in three parts for orchestra AMP(R)	
Five etudes for orchestra AMP(R)	14
Symphony (1965) AMP(R)	
SESSIONS, Roger	
Symphony no. 5 EBM(R)	16
Symphony no. 8 EBM(R)	
SIEGMEISTER, Elie	
Ozark set EBM(R)	25
1. Morning in the hills	
2. Camp meeting	
3. Lazy afternoon	
4. Saturday night	
STARER, Robert	
Six variations with 12 notes MCA(R)	5
STILL, William Grant	
Afro-American symphony (rev. 1969) BEL/MIL	24
STRANG, Gerald	
Intermezzo NME(R)	4
SUBOTNICK, Morton	
Play no. 2 (with 2-track tape) MCA(R)	
SWANSON, Howard	
Concerto for orchestra WEIN(R)	30

	Duration (min)
THOMSON, Virgil	
Boy fights alligator (fugue) from "Louisiana story") GS	4
Pilgrims & pioneers (from the film score of "Journey to America") GS	
TRAVIS, Roy	
Collage for orchestra OX(R)	6.5
WAGNER, Joseph	
Panorama MCA(R)	
WALKER, George	
Address for orchestra MCA(R)	19
WASHBURN, Robert	
Excursion OX	5
Festive overture OX	7
WEINER, Stanley	
Symphony no. 1 MCA(R)	31
WHEAR, Paul	
Catharsis suite LMP Debate. Reflection. Conclusion	6
Decade overture LMP	7
Quantum suite LMP	6.5
YARDUMIAN, Richard	
Armenian suite EV(R) (See also "(Orchestra) Small or Chamber")	16
Desolate city EV(R) Desolation. Renaissance	20
Symphonic suite EV(R)	16
Three pictographs EV(R)	18

ORCHESTRA-- FULL SYMPHONY WITH SOLO INSTRUMENT OR VOICE

	Solo	Duration (min)
AMRAM, David		
Concerto CFP(R)	hn	12
BENSON, Warren		
Quincy concerto MCA(R)	hn	NA

Orchestra: Full Symphony with Instr/Voice   119

	Solo	Duration (min)
BERGSMA, William Concerto GAL(R)	vln	21

BERNSTEIN, Seymour
Concerto ("in our time")   AMP(R)
  1. Gathering
  2. Lament for Vietnam
  3. Jubilation
	pno	11

BINKERD, Gordon A part of heaven: two romances for violin & orchestra B&H(R)	vln	16
BROWN, Rayner Concerto no. 2 WIM	org	13
CORIGLIANO, John Concerto GS(R)	pno	NA

CRESTON, Paul
Fantasy for piano & orchestra   GS(R)
  (See also "Keyboard--Piano,
  Four Hands")
	pno	NA

DELLO JOIO, Norman Fantasy & variations CF(R)	pno	NA

ERB, Donald
Concerto for solo percussion &
  orchestra   TP(R)
  (See also "Percussion")
	perc	NA

GOTTSCHALK, Louis Moreau
L'Union (arranged for piano &
  orchestra by Samuel Adler)   GS
  (See also "Keyboard--Piano,
  Four Hands")
	pno	NA

HEIDEN, Bernhard
Concerto for horn   AMP(R)
  1. Prelude, recitative & aria
  2. Theme & variations--finale
	hn	12

HELM, Everett Concerto AMP(R)	pno	NA
HILL, Alfred Concerto SMP(R)	vla	NA
IMBRIE, Andrew Concerto for violin SHAW(R)	vln	NA
KELLY, Robert Concerto for violin, Op. 46 GAL(R)	vln	23

	Solo	Duration (min)
KUBIK, Gail Concerto in D CHAP(R)	vln	25
LEES, Benjamin Piano concerto no. 2 B&H(R) The trumpet of the swan B&H(R)	pno Narr: text: E. B. White	25 18
LEVY, Marvin David One person B&H(R)	A; text: Elinor Wylie	19
LUKE, Ray Concerto for bassoon OX(R)	bsn	17
MacDOWELL, Edward (H. Wiley Hitchcock, Ed.) Concerto no. 2 in D-minor DCP	pno	26
MARTINO, Donald Concerto ECS(R)	pno	30
PARCHMAN, Gen Concerto for 1 percussionist SEM(R) Concerto for percussion ensemble SEM(R) 2nd concerto for percussion ensemble SEM(R)	perc perc ensemble perc ensemble	13 11 11
PERLE, George Concerto TP(R)	vlc	17
PERSICHETTI, Vincent A Lincoln address EV(R)	Narr; text: Lincoln's Second Inaugural Address	12
PISTON, Walter . Concerto for flute AMP(R) Fantasy for violin AMP(R)	fl vln	NA NA
PORTER, Quincy Concerto for viola AMP(R)	vla	NA
PYLE, Francis J. Concerto for harp S-C(R)	hp	NA
ROREM, Ned Poèmes pour la paix B&H(R) (For contents & authors of texts, see "(Voice) Solo") Six Irish poems SMPC(R) (For contents, see "Solo Vocal Music")	med voice med voice; text: George Darley (1795-1846)	12 12.5
ROSS, Walter Concerto for brass quintet & or- chestra B&H(R)		15

7. OPERA

Composer, Title and Publisher	Author of Text or Libretto	Type	Acts	Voices	Duration* (min)
AMRAM, David					
Twelfth night CFP(R)	Shakespeare	Comedy	2	2 S, m-S, 4 T, 3 Bar, 2 B-Bar, B	120
ARGENTO, Dominick					
Postcard from Morocco B&H(R)	John Donahue	Comedy	1	S, m-S, 2 T, Bar, B	90
The shoemaker's holiday B&H(R)	Based on play by Thomas Dekker; adaptation & additional lyrics by John Olon	Comedy--Ballad-opera	Prologue & 2 parts	2 S, m-S, A, T, 4 Bar	90
BRAY, John and John Nelson Barker (H. Wiley Hitchcock, Ed.)					
The Indian princess DCP	Based on story of Pocahontas & Captain John Smith	lyric drama		(Note: In this publication of this score, there are songs, choruses and incidental music. Two volumes in one--including the musical score and complete text of the drama.)	
CHADWICK, George W. (H. Wiley Hitchcock, Ed.)					
Judith DCP	Biblical	Drama		NA	60
HOIBY, Lee					
Summer and smoke BEL/MIL(R)	Lanford Wilson based on play by Tennessee Williams	Drama	2 (with prologue & epilogue)	3 S, 2 m-S, T, 3 Bar, 2 B-Bar, 3 speaking roles	120
HOVHANESS, Alan					
The travellers CFP	A. Hovhaness	Drama	1 scene	2 A, 3 B, ch	18
PASATIERI, Thomas					
Black widow BEL/MIL(R)	T. Pasatieri; based on novel, "Dos Madres" by Miguel de Unamuno	Drama	3	S, 2 m-S, T, Bar	100

	Solo	Duration (min)
I. Introduction & toccata		
II. Intermezzo notturno		
III. Variations		
STARER, Robert		
Concerto for violin & violon-	vln, vlc	19
cello MCA(R)		
STRICKLAND, Willy		
The trumpet shall sound! BEL/MIL	Narr; text: W. Strickland	9
THOMSON, Virgil		
Five songs from William Blake	med voice	NA
SMPC(R)		
The divine image. Tiger! Tiger!		
The land of dreams. The little		
black boy. "And those feet"		
WILDER, Alec		
Concerto AMP(R)	ob	NA
YARDUMIAN, Richard		
Piano concerto EV(R)	pno	18
Passacaglio. Recitative. Fugue		
Symphony no. 2 (Psalms) EV(R)	med voice; Biblical	28
Violin concerto EV(R)	vln	24

Composer, Title and Publisher	Author of Text or Libretto	Type	Acts	Voices	Dura-tion* (min)
Calvary BEL/ MIL(R)	W. B. Yeats	Religious drama	1	2 S, m-S, T, 3 Bar, 2 B	33
ROREM, Ned					
A childhood mir-acle (piano acc) SMPC	Elliott Stein; suggested by Hawthorne's "The snow image"	Drama	1	S, 2 m-S, A, T, B-Bar	33

8. BAND
(including wind symphony)

ALBERT, Thomas
  B flat piece MEDP   4

APPLEBAUM, Stan
  Marrakech bazaar: suite for   NA
    concert band BB
    I. Arrival of the caravan
    II. In the marketplace
    III. Muezzin's prayer & pro-
         cession of the faithful
    IV. Flashing scimitars

BALLARD, Louis W.
  Scenes from Indian life BI   5
    1. Two Indians--one Navajo,
        one Taos
    2. Building a wall--adobe
        house
    3. Indian friends finish the wall

BAMERT, Matthias
  Inkblot GS   5

BECK, John Ness
  Rhapsody for percussion &   7
    band BOS

BENNETT, David
  Flute royale (also available   3
    for flute & piano) CLB

BERKOWITZ, Sol
  Game of dance FM   4

BERNSTEIN, Leonard
  Shivaree, a fanfare for double   5
    brass ensemble & percussion

BLANK, Allan
  Concert piece for band AMP   5

BROWNE, Philip
  Sonoro & brioso for winds   7
    S-B

BUTTS, Carrol M.
  Flamingo trumpets for 3   3
    trumpets with band acc
    CLB
  Heritage West CLB   3
  Patrol '76 CLB   3
  Two chorales SMC   4
    1. Lo, how a rose e'er
        blooming (15th cent
        German)
    2. Salvation is created
        (Tschesnokoff)

CACAVAS, John
  Aria for winds BI   3
  Matador BI   2.5
  Shimmering flutes for flute   3
    trio & band (arr. by Don-
    ald E. Wilkes) SMC

CARTER, Charles
  Rhapsodic episode CLB   6
  Zodiac: concert march CLB   3

CARUSO, John
  Short prelude with perspec-   2.5
    tives CLB

CHANCE, John Barnes
  Elegy B&H   8

CHILDS, Barney
  Supposes: imago mundi   5
    MEDP

---

*Approximate. Duration indicated only when given in score.

	Duration* (min)		Duration* (min)

CRESTON, Paul
  Kalevala: a tone poem fan-   10
    tasy on six Finnish folk
    songs, Op. 95 GS

DANIELS, M. L.
  Concordium WB   3

DAVIS, Albert Oliver
  Songs of Nyasaland: a suite   7
    LMP
    Lament. Boat song. The hunt

DELLO JOIO, Norman
  Concertante for wind instru-   9.5
    ments EBM

DVORAK, Robert J.
  West Point symphony S-B   NA

EDMONDSON, John
  Pageantry overture CLB   5.5

ELWELL, Herbert
  The happy hypocrite, ballet   15
    suite CF

ERICKSON, Frank (trans.)
  Fugue & chorale on Yankee   4
    Doodle (trans. from orches-
    tral suite by Virgil Thomson)
    GS
  The incredible flutist (trans.   8
    from orchestral suite by
    Walter Piston) AMP
    Arrival of the circus. The
    circus. The flutist. Tango of
    the merchant's daughters.
    Spanish waltz. Polka finale
  Mysterious mountain (trans. of   6
    1st mov from Symphony no. 2
    by Alan Hovhaness) AMP

EVERETT, Thomas
  Feowertig Nu MEDP   NA

FARBERMAN, Harold
  Box AMC   NA

FINNEY, Ross Lee
  Summer in Valley City CFP   16.5
    Fanfare. Interlude. Parade.
    Games. Fireworks. Night

FRACKENPOHL, Arthur

  Quintagon EV   8
    Fanfare. Lullaby. Canon.
    Dirge. Rondo

GILLIS, Don
  Instant music FM   NA

GOLDSTEIN, William
  Colloquy for trombone &   5
    band SF

GRAYSON, Alan
  Cantico (a beguine) BI   4

GRIFFITH, Bus
  Centurion SMC   5
  Thesis SMC   4

GROSS, Charles
  Irish suite SHAW   7.5
    1. Brian Boru
    2. Nora
    3. The paycock

GRUNDMAN, Clare
  A classical overture B&H   6
  Festive piece B&H   6
  An Irish rhapsody B&H   6.5
  March: winds B&H   4

HADDAD, Don
  Mini-suite no. 1 SMC   3
    Pavane. March

HANSON, Howard
  Symphony no. 1--second   6
    movement (arr by com-
    poser) CF

HANSON, Robert
  Four French songs of the   7
    16th century SMC
    1. Troubadors
    2. Solemn ceremony
    3. Petite dance
    4. Festivals

HARTLEY, Walter S.
  Capriccio for trombone &   4
    band JBI

HEISENGER, Brent
  Statement SHAW   4

Duration*
(min)

Duration*
(min)

HERDER, Ronald
Säeta (rites & ceremonies)   NA
AB

HOVHANESS, Alan
Mysterious montain (trans.   6
by Frank Erickson) AMP
Prayer of Saint Gregory for   8
trumpet & band (trans. for
band by composer) PIC

IVES, Charles
"The Alcotts" (trans. from   8
piano sonata no. 2, "Con-
cord, Mass., 1840-1860,"
for band by Richard E.
Thurston) AMP
Circus band (trans. for band   3
& optional mixed chorus by
Jonathan Elkus) PIC
March intercollegiate two-step 5
for band JBI

JACKSON, Hanley
Tangents III for band & pre-
recorded tape SHAW

JAGER, Robert
Chorale & toccata EV   7

JOHNSON, Robert
Scenario--a scherzo for band   3
CLB

KARLINS, William
Passacaglia & rounds MEDP   4

KENNY, George
Allegro brilliante CLB   4
Band of gold CLB   3
Color burst CLB   3

KORTE, Karl
Gestures EV   5

KRAFT, Leo
Toccata GEN   5

KROEGER, Karl
Divertimento for band B&H   10
Variations on a hymn by   6.5
William Billings JBI

KURKA, Robert
The good soldier Schweik   20

suite, Op. 22 WEIN
Overture. Lament. March.
War dance. Pastoral.
Finale
Polka & waltz from The Good   6
Soldier Schweik WEIN

LATHAM, William P.
March five (with optional   3.5
parts for electric guitar
& contra-bass) CLB
Suite in Baroque style for   6.5
flute & band S-B
Allemande. Sarabande.
Minuet. Gigue

LEE, Dai-Keong
Prelude & hula COL   3

LUKE, Ray
Intrada & rondo LMP   4

McBETH, W. Francis
Reflections past SMC   3
The seventh seal SMC   14

McBRIDE, Robert
Mexican Rhapsody CF   8

MADDEN, Edward J.
Rock movement for band   7 (with-
EBM   out solos
(Note: Can be performed with or
without the standard rock instruments. Programming of ad lib
solos is optional.)

MAILMAN, Martin
Geometrics no. 1 SMC   5
In memoriam Frankie New-
ton, Op. 50 SMC   7

MALTBY, Richard
Ballad for clarinet & band   3
BEL/MIL
Esprit de corps BEL/MIL   3
Trenody (ten years after):
an elegiac tribute to the
memory of John F. Kennedy
WB. With Narr; text from ex-
cerpts from Inaugural Address

MITCHELL, Rex
Song for the young, a ballad   4
for band EBM

	Duration* (min)

	Duration* (min)

MORRISSEY, John J.
  Centennial suite   EBM   5
  Concerto grosso   CHAP   5

PENNINGTON, John
  Apollo (an aleatoric piece for   varies
    band) GS

PERSICHETTI, Vincent
  O cool is the valley: poem   6
    for band (after a poem by
    James Joyce) EV

PHILLIPS, Peter
  Round/Trip: a divertimento   varies
    for band BI

PISTON, Walter
  The incredible flutist   8
    (Suite for concert band tran-
    scribed by Frank Erickson)
    AMP
    Arrival of the circus. Circus
    march. The flutist. Tango of
    the merchant's daughters.
    Spanish waltz. Polka finale

POLYHAR, James D.
  1836: a new land--a new na-   7
    tion SMC
    Will you come to the bower.
    Green grow the lilacs. Fiesta.
    Azteca

PRESSER, William
  The devil's footprints   TP   5
  Symphony no. 2 for band   12
    TP
    Sonata. Passacaglia. Double
    fugue. Rondo

QUILLING, Howard
  Suite for alto saxophone &   25
    wind orchestra   ART(R)

RARIG, John
  Dance episode for saxophone   5
    & band   WIM

READ, Gardner
  Prayers of steel   COL   4

REED, Alfred
  A Northern legend   CLB   7.5

RHOADS, William E.
  Lament & march   SMC   4
  Latin elegy   SMC   4
  Pete's bossa nova   CLB   3

ROYER, Paul H.
  Fanfare festiva   CPC   3

SACCO, P. Peter
  Study for brass & percussion
    WIM
    (See also "Percussion")

SARRACCO, John
  Madriguera   AB   4

SCHICKELE, Peter
  Pavilion piece   EV   3

SCHULLER, Gunther
  Diptych for brass quintet   8
    & concert band   AMP
  Study in textures   AMP   7

SHULMAN, Alan
  Mazatlán   AB   6

SLATER, Neil
  Oratory for band   WB

SMITH, Julia
  Fanfare for alma mater   TP   4

SOSNIK, Harry
  The dogmas of the quiet   4
    past BI
  Starward (a space proces-   3
    sional for band) BI

SPEARS, Jared
  Chatham overture   SMC   5
  Chronica   CPC   5
  Kimberly overture   CPI   5
  March for moderns   CLB   3
  Prologue & pageant   SMC   5
  Third set for band   CLB   4
    Dance. Night song. Entry
    & minimarch

STUART, Hugh
  Samba & country dance   4
    SHAW

TANNER, Paul
  Aria for trombone & band WIM   5

	Duration* (min)			Duration* (min)

Concert duet for tenor &
bass trombone & band   WIM   5
Concerto for 2 trombones &   7.5
band

TATGENHORST, John
Tanglewood   CLB   3.5

THOMSON, Virgil
Fugue & chorale on Yankee   4
Doodle (transcribed for band
by Frank Erickson)   GS
Three portraits for band   GS
  1. Edges: A portrait of Robert
     Indiana
  2. Metropolitan Museum
     fanfare: A portrait of
     Florine
  3. Study piece: A portrait of
     a lady
(Note: Above available only
separately.)

THURSTON, Richard E. (trans)
"The Alcotts" (transcribed   8
from piano sonata no. 2,
"Concord, Mass., 1840-1860,"
by Charles Ives)   AMP

TUBB, Monte
Soundprint   LMP

TULL, Fisher
Antiphon   B&H   3.5
Terpsichore   B&H   3.5
Toccata   B&H   10.5

TUTHILL, Burnet
Fantasia for tuba or bass
trombone & band   CF

UBER, David
Symphonic fanfare for brass   3
choir   GS

WAGNER, Joseph
A festive fanfare for brass   3
& percussion   SF
(See also "Percussion")

WARD-STEINMAN, David
Gasparilla day (uncharacteris-   3
tic march for band)   EBM
Jazz tangents   SF   5

WASHBURN, Robert
Ceremonial music   OX   6

WATSON, Walter
Antiphony & chorale   LMP   6

WEBBER, Andrew Lloyd
Selections from "Jesus   7.5
Christ Superstar," arr by
Frederic J. Lewis with rock
rhythm section   MCA

WEISLING, Raymond
An original cold-flow   MEDP

WESTERGAARD, Peter
Tuckets & sennets: 6 etudes   12
for symphony band   AB
Sostenuto canons. Riffs. Brass
chords, pure & mixed. Fanfares with a trio. Hocketing.
Cantilena

WHEAR, Paul
Bellerophon: overture for   6
band   LMP
Elsinore: overture for band   6
LMP
Land of Lincoln: concert   4
march   LMP
Proscenium overture of this   9.5
time   LMP
Stonehenge symphony for band   17
LMP
Solstice. Evocation. Sacrifice

WILLIAMS, Clifton
Variation overture   LMP   5

WILLIAMS, Edgar Warren
Prologue   LMP   6

WILLIAMS, John T.
Sinfonietta for winds & per-   17
cussion   MCA(R)
(See also "Percussion")

ZONN, Paul
Kyklos   MEDP

KEY TO PUBLISHERS

AB Alexander Broude, Inc.
225 West 57th Street
New York, N.Y. 10019

ABP Abington Press
201 8th Avenue South
Nashville, Tennessee 37202

AMC Alfred Music Co., Inc.
75 Channel Drive
Port Washington, N.Y. 11050

AMP Associated Music Publishers, Inc.
866 Third Avenue
New York, N.Y. 10022
Agents overseas:
Albania, Austria, Bulgaria,
Czechoslovakia, Greece,
Hungary, Poland, Rumania,
Yugoslavia:...Doblinger,
Vienna, Austria
Australia:...Allan & Co.
Ltd., Melbourne
Belgium, Netherlands,
Switzerland, West Germany:
...B. Schott's Soehne,
Mainz, Germany
Denmark, Finland, Norway,
Sweden:...Wilhelm Hansen,
Copenhagen, Denmark
France:...Editions Max
Eschig, Paris
Italy:...G. Ricordi, Milan
Spain:...Union Musical
Española, Madrid
United Kingdom & Irish
Free State:...Schott & Co.
Ltd., London

ARNO Arno Press
330 Madison Avenue
New York, N.Y. 10017

ART Artisan Music Press
Box 75
Cornwall, N.Y. 12518

AUG Augsburg Publishing House
426 South Fifth Street
Minneapolis, Minnesota 55415

BB Broude Brothers Limited
Music Publishers
56 West 45th Street
New York, N.Y. 10036

BCM Bowdoin College Music Press
Brunswick, Maine 04011

BEL/MIL
Belwin-Mills Publishing Corp.
Melville, N.Y. 11746
Divisions:
Franco Colombo Publica-
tions; J. Fischer & Bro.;
H.W. Gray and selling agt.
for Marks Music Corp.
Exclusive Distributors to the
Music Trade: Music Minus
One; Jobete Music Co., Inc.
Sole Agents for the United
States of America:
Paris...Amphion, S.A.R.L.
London...Belwin-Mills, Ltd.
Bologna...F. Bongiovanni
Paris...Editions Bornemann
Celle...Moeck Verlag
London,..Novello & Co. Ltd.
Florence... Otos, S.A.S.
Milan, Paris, Frankfurt,
London, Sydney, Toronto,
Buenos Aires, Sao Paul, Mex-
ico City...G. Ricordi & C.,
Mainz...B. Schott's Soehne
London...Schott & Co., Ltd.
Hamburg... Musikverlage
Hans Sikorski
Milan...Casa Musicale Sonzo-
gno, Basel...Symphonia
Verlag

B&H Boosey & Hawkes
30 West 57th Street
New York, N.Y. 10019

(for rental); for sales, address:
Oceanside, New York, N.Y.
11572
  Agents overseas:
    Australia:...Boosey & Hawkes
    (Australia) Pty. Ltd.,Sydney
    Austria:...Theater-Verlag
    Eirich, Vienna
    Belgium & France:...Boosey
    & Hawkes, S.A., Paris
    Canada:...Boosey & Hawkes
    (Canada) Ltd., Toronto
    Denmark:...Wilhelm Hansen,
    Copenhagen
    England:...Boosey & Hawkes
    Music Publishers Ltd.,
    London
    Germany & Switzerland:...
    Boosey & Hawkes GmbH,
    Bonn
    Hungary:...Kultura, Buda-
    pest
    Italy:...Carisch S.p.a.,
    Milan
    Netherlands:...Albersen &
    Co., The Hague
    Norway:...Norsk Musikfor-
    lag a/s, Oslo
    South Africa:...Boosey &
    Hawkes (S. Africa) Pty.
    Ltd., Johannesburg
    South America:...Barry &
    Cia. Buenos Aires, Argen-
    tina
    Spain:...Robert Achard,
    Madrid
    Sweden:...Carl Gehrmans
    Musikforlag, Stockholm

BI   Bourne Co. (formerly Bourne,
    136 West 52nd Street   Inc.)
    New York, N.Y. 10019

BOS   The Boston Music Company
    116 Boylston Street
    Boston, Mass. 02116

CAP   Composers' Autograph Publi-
    cation
    1527-1/2 N. Vine Street
    Los Angeles, Calif. 90028
        or
    Box 7103
    Cleveland, Ohio 44128

CBP   Claude Benny Press
    Box 461, Milton Junction
    Wisconsin 53563

CF   Carl Fischer, Inc.
    56-62 Cooper Square
    New York, N.Y. 10003

CFP   C. F. Peters Corporation
    373 Park Avenue South
    New York, N.Y. 10016
    Agents overseas:
      Austria & Germany:...C. F.
      Peters, Frankfurt/Main
      Belgium:...Schott Frères,
      Brussels
      Norway:...Harold Lyche &
      Co., Oslo
      Switzerland:...Edition
      Eulenburg, Zurich
      All other countries:...
      Hinrichsen Edition Ltd.,
      London
      with following exception:
      Countries of Western Hem-
      isphere, Japan and The
      Philippines, which should
      order C. F. Peters publica-
      tions from the office in
      New York, N.Y.

CHAP   Chappell & Co., Inc.
    609 Fifth Avenue
    New York, N.Y. 10017
    Agents overseas:
      Australia:...Chappell & Co.
      Ltd., Sydney
      England:...Chappell & Co.
      Ltd., London
      France:...S. A. F. Chappell,
      Paris

CHH   Charles H. Hansen Music Corp.
    Miami Beach, Florida

CLB   C. L. Barnhouse Co.
    Music Publishers
    Oskaloosa, Iowa 52577

COL   Franco Colombo Publications
    A Division of Belwin/Mills
    Publishing Corp.
    Melville, N.Y. 11746
    Agents overseas:
      Australia:...G. Ricordi &
      Co., Sydney
      Argentina:...Ricordi Amer-
      icana S.A., Buenos Aires
      Brazil:...Ricordi Brasileira
      S.A., São Paulo
      Canada:...Leeds Music Ltd.,
      Toronto
      England:...G. Ricordi & Co.

(London) Ltd. London
France:... Edition Salabert,
Paris
Germany:...G. Ricordi &
Co., Frankfurt/Main
Italy:...G. Ricordi & Co.,
Milan
Mexico:...G. Ricordi & Co.,
Mexico City, D. F.
Switzerland:...Symphonia
Verlag, Basel

CPC M. M. Cole Publishing Co.
251 East Grand Avenue
Chicago, Illinois   60611

CPE Composer/Performer Edition
330 University Avenue
Davis, California   95616

CPH Concordia Publishing House
3558 South Jefferson Avenue
St. Louis, Missouri   63118

CPI The Composers Press, Inc.
c/o Seesaw Music Corporation
177 East 87th Street
New York, N.Y.   10028

CTW C. T. Wagner Music Publishers
1753 Hobart Street, N.W.
P.O. Box 21127
Washington, D.C.   20009

DCP Da Capo Press
227 West 17th Street
New York, N.Y.   10011

EBM Edward B. Marks Music Corp.
c/o Belwin/Mills Pub. Corp.
Melville, N.Y.   11746
Agent overseas:
England:...Schott & Co.,
Ltd., London

ECS E.C. Shirmer Music Company
112 South Street
Boston, Mass.   02111

EM   Edition Musicus
333 West 52nd Street
New York, N.Y.   10019

EV   Elkan-Vogel Co.
A subsidiary of Theodore
Presser Co.

Presser Place
Bryn Mawr, Pa.   19010
Sole agents in U.S.A.
Durand Edition
Henry Lemoine & Co.,
Jean Jobert
Editions Philippo. Ars Nova
Organ catalogue: Edition
Heuwekemeijer.

FAM Fine Arts Music Press
Tulsa, Oklahoma

FER Ferol Publications
Box 6007
Alexandria, Va.   22306

FLAM Harold Flammer, Inc.
c/o Shawnee Press
Delaware Gap, Pa.   18327

FM   Frank Music Corp.
c/o The Boston Music Co.
116 Boylston Street
Boston, Mass.   02116
Agents overseas:
Brazil:...Fermata do Brazil
LTDA, São Paulo
Canada:...Frank Music Co.
(Canada) Ltd., Toronto
England:...Frank Music
Co. Ltd., London
Italy:...Edizioni Frank
Music S.r.l., Milan
Re: Mexico:...Ariston Mu-
sic Inc., New York, N.Y.

GAL Galaxy Music Corporation
2121 Broadway
New York, N.Y.   10023
Agents overseas:
England:...Galliard Ltd.,
London
Germany:...Heinrichshofen's
HWG verlag, Wilhelms-
haven

GEN General Music Pub. Co., Inc.
The Boston Music Co.
(sole distributor)
116 Boylston Street
Boston, Mass.   02116

GS   G. Schirmer, Inc.
609 Fifth Avenue
New York, N.Y.   10017
Agents overseas:

Australia:... Allan & Co.,
Ltd., Melbourne (for orch
& opera rental materials)
Austria:... Universal Edition,
Vienna (for orch & opera
rental materials)
Denmark, Norway, Sweden:
... Wilhelm Hansen,
Copenhagen
England:... Chappell & Co.
Ltd., London (materials for
sale); J. Curwen & Sons,
Ltd; Faber Music Ltd.
France also for Belgium,
Czechoslovakia, Greece,
Hungary, Israel, Poland,
Portugal, Spain & Yugo-
slavia:... Edition Salabert,
Paris (for orch & opera
rentals)
Germany:... Anton Benjamin,
Hamburg (for orch rentals);
August Seith, Munich (ma-
terials for sale)
Italy:... G. Ricordi & Co.,
Milan
Netherlands:... Albersen &
Co., The Hague (for orch
rentals)

HAR   Hargail Music Press
157 West 57th Street
New York, N.Y.   10019

HE   Henri Elkan Music Publisher
1316 Walnut Street
Philadelphia, Pa.   19107
Agent overseas:
Belgium:... metropolis
Frankrijklei 24, Antwerpen 1

HME   Helios Music Edition
c/o Mark Foster Music Co.
Box 783
Marquette, Michigan   49855

HWG   The H.W. Gray Company, Inc.
A Div. of Belwin/Mills Pub.
Melville, N.Y.   11746   Corp.
Agent overseas:
England:... Novello & Co.,
Ltd., London

IP   Independent Publishers
215 East 42nd Street
New York, N.Y.   10019

JBI   Joseph Boonin, Inc.
831 Main Street
Hackensack, N.J.   07601

JF   J. Fischer & Bro.
A Div. of Belwin/Mills Pub.
Melville, N.Y.   11746

KAL   Edwin F. Kalmus
P.O. Box 1007
Commack, N.Y.   11725

KING Robert King Music Company
North Easton, Mass.   02356

KMI   Kendor Music, Inc.
Delevan, N.Y.   14042

KSM   KSM Publishing Co.
507 North Willomet
Dallas, Texas   75208

L-G   Lawson-Gould Music Publishers
Inc., G. Schirmer, sole
selling agent.
609 Fifth Avenue
New York, N.Y.   10017

LMP   Ludwig Music Publishing Co.
557-67 East 140th Street
Cleveland, Ohio   44110

LPI   Leblanc Publications, Inc.
Kenosha, Wisconsin   53140

LYRA Lyra Music Publishing Co.
43 West 61st Street
New York, N.Y.   10023

MCA   Music Corporation of America
543 West 43rd Street
New York, N.Y.   10036

MEDP Media Press
P.O. Box 895
Champaign, Ill.   61820

MJQ   MJQ Music, Inc.
200 West 57th Street
New York, N.Y. 10019

MM   McGinnis & Marx
201 West 86th St., Apt. 706
New York, N.Y.   10024

MP   Music for Percussion, Inc.
c/o Plymouth Music Co., Inc.
17 West 60th Street
New York, N.Y.   10023

MPC   Mark Press Company
c/o Mark Foster Music Co.
Box 783
Marquette, Michigan   49855

NAK   Neil A. Kjos Music Publishers
525 Busse Highway
Park Ridge, Illinois   60068

OKM   Okra Music Corp.
c/o Seesaw Music Corporation
177 East 87th Street
New York, N.Y.   10028

OPB   O. Pagani and Bros., Inc.
289 Bleecker St.
New York, N.Y.   10014

OX   Oxford University Press
200 Madison Avenue
New York, N.Y.   10016

PIC   Peer International Corporation
636 Eleventh Avenue
New York, N.Y.   10036

RAL   Raldor Music
22 Walden Avenue
Jericho, N.Y.   11753

RBB   Robert B. Brown Music Co.
1709 No. Kenmore Avenue
Hollywood, California   90027

RDR   R. D. Row Music Company
353 Newbury Street
Boston, Mass. 02115

RMP   Rochester Music Photocopy Co.
12 Worthington Road
Rochester, N.Y.   14622

S-B   Summy-Birchard Company
(all orders & requests are
    handled through Educational
    Music Bureau, Inc.)
1834 Ridge Avenue
Evanston, Illinois   60204

S-C   Scully-Cutter Urtext Editions
1315 4th Street Southeast
Minneapolis, Minnesota 55414

SEM   Seesaw Music Corporation
177 East 87th Street
New York, N.Y.   10028

SF   Sam Fox Publishing Co., Inc.
1841 Broadway
New York, N.Y.   10023

SHAW   Shawnee Press, Inc.
Delaware Water Gap, Pa.
18327

SMC   Southern Music Company
1100 Broadway--P.O. Box 329
San Antonio, Texas   78206

SMP   The Sacred Music Press
501 East 3rd Street
Dayton, Ohio   45401

SMPC   Southern Music Publishing Co.
636 Eleventh Avenue
New York, N.Y.   10036
Agents overseas:
    Australia:... Southern Music
     Pub. Co. (Australasia)
     Pty. Ltd., Sydney
    Canada:... Southern Music
     Pub. Co. (Canada) Ltd.,
     Montreal
    Central & South America:
     ...Ricordi Americana,
     S.A. Buenos Aires, Argen-
     tina
    European countries:... Peer
     Musikverlag GmbH, Ham-
     burg, Germany
    Japan:... Nippon Gakki Co.
     Ltd. Gakufu, Ginza 7-1,
     Chuo-Ku, Tokyo
    Mexico:... Promotoro His-
     pana Americana de Musica,
     Mexico City, D.F.
    New Zealand:... Southern
     Music Pub. Co. (New Zea-
     land) Pty. Ltd., Auckland
     C. 1

TP   Theodore Presser Company
Presser Place
Bryn Mawr, Pa.   19010
Agents overseas:
    Austria:... Universal Edition,
     Vienna; Haydn Mozart
     Press, Vienna; Philhar-
     monia Pocket Scores,
     Vienna

England:... Universal Edition,
London
France:... Editions Musicales
Transatlantiques, Paris;
Heugel & Cie, Paris
Germany:... Impero Verlag
Wilhelmshaven
Switzerland:... Universal
Edition, Zurich

UCP   University of California Press
Berkeley, California   94720

UMP   University of Miami Press
Miami, Florida   33124

VAL   The New Valley Music Press
Sage Hall, Smith College
Northampton, Mass.   01060

VB   Volkwein Bros., Inc.
117 Sandusky Street
Pittsburgh, Pa.   15212

WEIN Weintraub Music Company
33 West 60th Street
New York, N.Y.   10023

WIM   Western International Music, Inc.
2859 Holt Avenue
Los Angeles, California   90034

WIT   M. Witmark and Sons
488 Madison Avenue
New York, N.Y.   10022

WLP   World Library Publications, Inc.
2145 Central Parkway
Cincinnati, Ohio   45214

WMC   Walton Music Corp.
17 West 60th Street
New York, N.Y.   10023

WME   Waldwick Music Editions
123 Bergen Avenue
Waldwick, N.J.   07463

WB   Warner Bros. Publications, Inc.
75 Rockefeller Plaza
New York, N.Y.   10020

YUP   Yale University Press
92A Yale Station
New Haven, Conn.   06520

AMENDMENTS

To the Second Edition and to the (First) Supplement

In order to make further corrections in the Second Edition and to list corrections for the First Supplement as well, some amendments are listed below. Not only have errors of omission and commission been corrected, but publisher designations have also been changed. These latter changes reflect the exchange of various publishing rights among the publishers as well as errors in both editions.

Second Edition

page

109 SIEGMEISTER: change title "I see a land, (etc.)" to "This is our land (etc.)"

150 SCHUMAN: after "Deo ac veritati" change GS to TP

191 DELLO JOIO: after "Laudation" change EBM to B&H

201 BABBITT: after "Composition for viola and piano" change AMP to CFP

220 HAIEFF: after "Quartet No. 1" change B&H to CFP

239 REIF: after "Wind spectrum" change GEN to SEM

277 FULEIHAN: after "Rhapsody" change CF to B&H

278 HOVHANESS: after "Talin" change CFP to AMP

285 DUKELSKY: after "Symphony no. 3" change COL(R) to CF(R)

289 LA MONTAINE: after "Canons for orchestra" and "Jubilant overture" change PJS(R) to CF(R)

300 MARTINO: change duration of "Concerto" from 18 to 27

315 KIRK: after "Smokey Mountain suite" change S-B to SMC

317 NIBLOCK: after "Soliloquy and dance" change S-B to SMC

First Supplement

vi after "**BAND" insert "ADDENDUM TO SUPPLEMENT NO. 1   115"

36 PINKHAM: after "I was glad" change AMP to ECS

44 ADLER: the publisher of "In nature's ebb and flow" is PIC

63 BROWN: after "Corroboree" change AMP to TP

68 ALEXANDER: change spelling of first name to "Josef" change "Melody for flute" to "Monody for flute"

70 DONATO: after "Sonata" change SMPC to SMC

135

73   ALEXANDER: change spelling of first name to "Josef"

76   READ: after "Sonoric fantasie No 3" change AB to SEM

83   UBER: change "Suite for four hours" to "Suite for four horns"

108 DELLO JOIO: duration of "Songs of Abelard" is 15.5 min
     ERB: after "Space music" change FM to TP

111 READ: duration of "Dunlap's Creek" is 5 min

115 SEIGMEISTER: after "Madam to you" change SEM to CFP

116 SYDEMAN: delete "Composition (with string quartet and tape)"; it is
     the same composition as the following title

117 DIEMENTE: change author of text to "Elizabeth Randall-Mills"

120 REIF: duration for "Triple city" is 20 min
     SYDEMAN: duration for "Prometheus" is 25 min

121 FULEIHAN: after "Sonata No. 9" change SMPC to SMC

123 SYDEMAN: after "Concert piece," delete (also with string orchestra)

126 DIEMENTE: instr for "Celebration for wind ensemble" is 3,3,3,4,3
     sax; 4,3,5,2; 3 perc

AUTHOR INDEX

ABELARD, Peter 4, 44
ADAMS, Marjorie 19
AGEE, James 19, 55
AKIBA, Omar Rabbi 41
ARMOUR, Richard 36
ARNOLD, Matthew 45
AUDEN, W. H. 18
AUSTIN, William 19, 33

BABBITT, Milton 44
BACH, Johann Sebastian 1
BALDWIN, William 34
BARING-GOULD, S., alt 17, 54
BARNARD, Mary 11
BARTON, Emily 3
BASHO 8
BATES, Arlo 2, 3
BAX, Clifford 45
BEAUMONT, John 37, 61
BEAUMONT, Joseph 40
BECK, John Ness 13
BEGLARIAN, Grant 72
BELL, Maurice 33
BELLOC, Hilaire 39
BENÉT, Stephen Vincent 7
BENNETT, Claudia 13, 54
BERNSTEIN, Leonard 14
BEVERIDGE, Thomas 44, 45
BIBLE 2, 4, 5, 7, 8, 10, 11, 12,
    13, 14, 18, 19, 20, 21, 22, 23,
    24, 26, 27, 28, 29, 30, 31, 32,
    33, 34, 35, 36, 37, 38, 39, 40,
    41, 42, 43, 45, 46, 47, 50, 51,
    54, 55, 56, 57, 58, 59, 60, 61,
    62, 121, 122
BLAKE, William 5, 7, 16, 24, 28,
    45, 51, 121
BLANCO, Joseph 17
BOETHIUS 45
BOMEN, Lord 7
BORTHWICK, Jane Laurie 45
BRADBURY, Ray 38
BRADSTREET, Ann 45
BRINGLE, Terry 20, 46
BROWN, Bartholomew 30
BROWN, Rayner 16

BROWNING, Elizabeth Barrett 22
BRUBECK, Dave & Iola 17
BRUCE, Michael 51
BRYANT, Florence 7
BURNS, Robert 33, 45
BUSON, Taniquchi 8
BUSON-SOGYO 8
BYNNER, Witter 45
BYRON, Lord 4, 10

CALABRO, Leontina 17
CAMPION, Thomas 16, 50
CAREW, Thomas 24
CARROLL, Lewis 47, 58, 98
CHAUCER, Geoffrey 37, 51, 61
CHESTERTON, G. K. 45
CHIYO 8
CHOPIN, Frederic 1
CHRISTY, Marian 19
CLARK, Axton 21, 28
COLE, John 30
COLERIDGE, Mary E. 33
COLGRASS, Michael 3, 18, 54
COLUMBA 38
CONVERSE, Ruth 44
COOPER, William 30
COWPER, William 16, 37, 43
CRAPSEY, Adelaide 6
CRASHAW, Richard 40, 45
CUMMINGS, E. E. 4, 8, 12, 28,
    31, 42, 43, 49, 52
CUNNINGHAM, Arthur 18, 54
CUSHING (Cardinal) 19

DARLEY, George 10
DAURAT, Jean 10
DAVIES, Sir J. 33
de BAIF, Jean Antoine 10
DEBUSSY, Claude 1
DEKKER, Thomas 122
de MAGNY, Olivier 10
DE MORLAIX, Bernard 34, 60
d'ORLEANS, Charles 3
de RONSARD, Pierre 3, 10
de UNAMUNO, Miguel 122

137

STRONGWOLF, Chief Joseph 12
SUCKLING, Sir John 19, 28

TEASDALE, Sara 22, 32, 46, 47
TENNYSON, Alfred Lord 10
THOMAS, Dylan 1
THOMSON, Samuel 30
THOREAU, Henry David 11
THORNE, Francis 11
TICHBORNE, Chidiock 4
TREVELYAN, R. C. 14, 17, 54
TU-FU 45
TWAIN, Mark 50, 54
TZUR, Moos 41

UDA (Emperor) 4
UNTERMEYER, Jean Starr 8

Van HOSEN, Wanda Marine 5
VAUGHAN, Henry 16
VERLAINE, Paul 3

WALLER, Edmund 24
WATTS, Isaac 17, 26, 33, 34, 39,
    40, 43, 61
WESLEY, Charles 32, 37, 45
WHITE, E. B. 120
WHITMAN, Walt 9, 29, 38, 45, 58
WHITTIER, John Greenleaf 27
WILBUR, Richard 11
WILLIAMS, Tennessee 2, 122
WILLEY, George A. 33
WILSON, Lanford 122
WORDSWORTH, William 10, 24
WU, Wei Ying 45
WYATT, Sir Thomas 12
WYLIE, Elinor 7, 120

YEATS, William Butler 10, 11, 20,
    27, 51, 123
YOSE (Emperor) 4
YOUNG, Gordon 43
YOUNG, Roland 7

ZOLBROD, Leon 10

COMPOSER INDEX

ADLER, Samuel (1928-) 43, 75, 76, 81, 101
AHROLD, Frank 12, 53
ALBERT, Stephen 12, 53
ALBERT, Thomas 80, 95
ALBRIGHT, William (1944-) 67, 85
ALEXANDER, Josef (1910-) 12, 73, 80, 85, 95
ALLCOCK, Stephen 12
AMRAM, David (1930-) 93, 118, 122
ANDERSON, Gillian (Ed.) 15, 35
APPLEBAUM, Stan 124
ARGENTO, Dominick (1927-) 1, 44, 53, 116, 122
ARNATT, Ronald 67
ASHLEY, Robert (1930-) 85
ATHEY, Ralph 85
AUSTIN, Larry 63, 76
AVSHALOMOV, Jacob (1919-) 12

BABBITT, Milton (1916-) 1, 44, 72, 84
BACH, Jan 95
BACON, Ernst (1898-) 44
BAIRD, James 104
BAKER, R. 107
BAKSA, Robert (1938-) 12
BALLARD, Louis W. 12, 124
BAMERT, Matthais 93, 124
BANKS, Robert (1930-) 13
BARAB, Seymour (1921-) 1
BARBER, Samuel (1910-) 13, 53, 116
BARKER, John Nelson 122
BARNES, Edward Shippen 69
BARR, John 67
BARTOW, Nevett 63, 67
BASSETT, Leslie (1923-) 13, 53, 63, 72, 85, 116
BATES, Arlo 2
BAUMGARTNER, Leroy 70
BAVICCHI, John (1922-) 2, 13, 63, 76, 91, 99, 104
BECK, John Ness (1930-) 2, 13, 53, 63, 104, 124
BECKER, John J. 84

BEERMAN, Burton 85
BEESON, Jack (1921-) 44, 49, 63, 66
BEGLARIAN, Grant (1927-) 72
BELLSON, Louis 104
BENNETT, Claudia 13, 54
BENNETT, David 124
BENSON Warren (1924-) 2, 78, 84, 118
BERGSMA, William (1921-) 116, 119
BERKOWITZ, Saul 116
BERKOWITZ, Sol 124
BERNSTEIN, Leonard (1918-) 14, 54, 72, 101, 104, 124
BERNSTEIN, Seymour 63, 119
BERRY, Wallace (1928-) 72, 73, 75, 77, 85
BETTS, Donald 14
BEVERIDGE, Thomas (1938-) 2, 44, 45, 49
BEVERSDORF, Thomas (1924-) 14, 75, 80, 85, 95, 99, 101
BIALOWSKY, Marshall (1923-) 63, 76, 78
BIELAWA, Herbert 14
BIGGS, John 92
BILLINGS, William (1746-1800) 14, 35, 36, 49, 50, 126
BINGHAM, Seth (1882-1972), 16, 69
BINKERD, Gordon (1916-) 16, 45, 50, 119
BLANCHARD, William G. 67
BLANK, Allan (1925-) 91, 124
BLATTER, Alfred 81, 84, 101
BLOCK, Robert Paul 98
BOATWRIGHT, Harold (1918-) 85
BOCK, Fred 2
BODA, John (1922-) 80
BOLCOM, William (1938-) 63, 85
BOTTJE, Will Gay (1925-) 99
BOWMAN, Carl 16, 54
BOYD, Jack 50, 54
BRADLEY, Ruth 2, 45
BRAY, John 122
BRITAIN, Radie (1903-) 74
BROSCH, Barry 72
BROWN, Earle (1926-) 83, 85, 116